"This is a gem of a book! Dr. Nedd's reader-friendly writing style mirrors his personality – engaging, inspirational, and upbeat. His expertise in the field of stress and his wisdom as a family physician leap from the pages. Most important, he gives the reader the tools and confidence to help themselves and to feel whole again. I would like to see this book in every physician's waiting room."

– MICHAEL MYERS, MD, FRCPC,
Clinical Professor, Department of Psychiatry, University of British Columbia and Past President, Canadian Psychiatric Association

"I would highly recommend Power Over Stress *to anyone who wishes to see an immediate change in their stress level, and wishes to find a practical, user-friendly approach to dealing with stressors BEFORE they become significant problems."*

– RUSSELL KENNEDY, MD

D0042845

POWER OVER STRESS

KENFORD NEDD, M.D.

35 Quick Prescriptions for Mastering the Stress in Your Life

QP PRESS
TORONTO, CANADA

First published in Canada in 2003 by QP Press
This edition published in 2004 by QP Press
Copyright © Kenford Nedd, M.D.

All rights reserved. The use of any part of this publication reproduced, transmitted in any form or by any means, electronic, mechanical, recording, or otherwise, or stored in a retrieval system, without the prior consent of the publisher, is an infringement of the copyright law. In the case of photocopying or other reprographic copying of the material, a licence must be obtained from the Canadian Copyright Licensing Agency (Access Copyright) before proceeding.

National Library of Canada Cataloguing in Publication

Nedd, Kenford
Power over stress : 35 quick prescriptions for mastering the stress in your life / Kenford Nedd.

ISBN 0-9733291-0-6

1. Stress management. I. Title.

RA785.N42 2003 155.9'042 C2003-903097-0

3 4 5 NA GEN WC 07 06 05 04

Redesign and production supervision: *Mad Dog Design Connection Inc.*
Printed in Canada by *Webcom*

The Author has used his best efforts in preparing this book. The publication contains the opinions and ideas of the Author and is designed to provide useful advice in regard to the subject matter covered. The Author and/or Publisher are not engaged in rendering medical, therapeutic, or other professional services in this publication. This publication is not intended to provide a basis for action in particular circumstances without consideration by a competent professional. The Author makes no representations or warranties with respect to the accuracy or completeness of the contents of this book and specifically disclaims any implied warranties of merchantability or fitness for a particular purpose. There are no warranties that extend beyond the descriptions contained in this paragraph. No warranty may be created or extended by sales representatives or written sales materials. The accuracy and completeness of the information provided in this publication and the opinions stated herein are not guaranteed or warranted to produce any specific results, and the advice and strategies contained herein may not be suitable for every individual. The Author shall not be liable for any loss of profit or any other commercial damages including but not limited to special, incidental, consequential, or other damages.

The people and situations depicted in this book are fictitious. Any resemblance to persons living or dead is coincidental.

For information concerning the purchase of additional copies of this book, please contact:

Dr. Kenford Nedd at info@stressdoctors.com or telephone 604.632.9500

I would like to thank
Mariela, Kaiyo, Keymo, and Kara
for their love and support.

ACKNOWLEDGEMENT

I am enormously grateful to my editor, Susan Girvan, for her dedication and insightful work in the preparation of this book. Susan, you are great, and great to work with.

CONTENTS

PART TWO

PART THREE
Stress-Proofing for Life 81

PREFACE:
A MESSAGE FROM KENFORD NEDD, M.D.

I AM A MEDICAL doctor and have been practising in the field of family medicine and stress-related disorders for more than 17 years. My job is to help patients severely affected by stress—whether it stems from financial setbacks, a troublesome relationship, or difficulties at work. I have seen too many patients suffering needlessly from illnesses brought on by the stress in their lives. Often the stress gets expressed as depression; sometimes physical symptoms such as migraines or heart disease predominate. Experience with these patients has taught me what works and what doesn't when it comes to defusing stress. I am going to share with you techniques and skills that will help you overcome the stress in your life.

In addition to my practice as a doctor, I speak internationally on the subject of stress and have addressed people from all walks of life—executives, mayors, and prime ministers among them. My goal is to teach all of you how to defeat the stress reaction and stress-proof your lives.

I want to give you a clear understanding of the dangers of a stress reaction, and then tell you how to avoid them. I have included practical exercises—my prescriptions—that you can use to avoid the consequences of stress that I treat in my clinic.

I write prescriptions every day for drugs that help people get better. The prescriptions in this book, however, are not for drugs. They are behavioral and physiological tricks that you can use in times of stress.

I am very excited about sharing this material with you because I know that it has helped many people navigate stressful situations. If you use the prescriptions in this book, you will be able to build the kind of mental and physical strength that will keep you from falling ill when potentially stressful troubles strike.

Today, more than ever, we all need practical ways to deal with stress. Stress control used to be desirable for a busy person, but now it is a binding obligation for anyone who wants to succeed and be healthy and happy at the same time. Stressful situations—stressors—are inevitable, but the resulting stress and illness are not. And if you do not manage the emotional, chemical, and physiological changes that usually occur in your body when you are faced with stressful situations, you will become sick. Learn to master the response of your inner terrain—your thoughts and emotions—and your behavior when the events in your life seem overwhelming and difficult. That is what you will be doing in the following pages.

You will find practical techniques to master your reactions to stressors. You will learn to control not just the common reactions like muscle tension, but you will learn to control and manage variables like your blood pressure, your heart rate, the ability of your white blood cells to fight germs, and ways to improve the clarity and sturdiness of your memory. Not all of the techniques in this book will appeal to you, or you may be doing some of them already. Nevertheless, I advise you to read through the whole book at least once because many of the techniques build on ones that have been introduced earlier. Then go back and concentrate on the techniques that will benefit you the most.

So, what do you need? What will make you stronger mentally when it comes to dealing with stressors? What physical exercises would really help? Keep reading and looking for the practical steps that can help you change your life and your health for the better.

INTRODUCTION

"LIFE IS ONE darn thing after another." This is about the most accurate definition of life that I have ever heard. Each "darn thing" is basically a stressor with the potential to spoil your day, your week, your year, and sometimes your whole life. The reality is that as long as you are alive, potentially irritating events and situations are inevitable.

The trick to living well lies not in avoiding stressors, but in knowing how to deal with them. You should know how to strengthen your physiology in such a way that the "darn things" that crop up from time to time will not rattle your composure or weaken your physical health.

While stressors can be large or small, which type of stressors do you think cause the most trouble and the most disease? Major or minor ones?

I don't think you need a Ph.D. to figure out that in life, it is the minor, mundane, repetitive difficulties that cause the most stress. A man who had walked from New York to San Francisco said that the toughest thing he had to deal with was not walking up the hills or crossing the hot, barren stretches of desert. His biggest stressor was sand in his shoes. Likewise, beware of those little irritants that trigger changes in your body that can lead to serious illness. In the field of stress-related disease, little things don't mean a lot. They mean almost everything.

From now on, pay attention to how you react to the little irritants in your life. Elephants don't bite, you see; it is the tiny mosquitoes that do.

I QUICK STRESS QUIZ

How Stressed Are You?

How many of these statements describe you and your life?

(1) There are many people in my life making demands on my time and energy.

(2) I am always in a hurry, and I'm often running late.

(3) I'm quick to notice loud noises and they irritate me a lot.

(4) I'm often caught off guard by events and demands.

(5) I often feel that I have no control over what's happening to me.

(6) I usually keep my feelings to myself; it's more important to get on with the job at hand.

(7) When someone else is talking, I try to hurry the conversation along. I sometimes finish sentences for others.

(8) I get impatient when I see something being done more slowly than I think it can be done.

(9) I get very irritable if I am delayed or have to wait. I hate lineups and slow drivers.

(10) I do one (or all) of the following often: fiddle with my hair, scratch, touch my nose, shake my legs, tap my foot, or doodle.

(11) I like to be busy. I always carry something to do. If nothing's planned for the evening or the weekend, I take work home.

(12) I am competitive by nature. People who know me well think of me as a hard-driving individual.

(13) I can stay alert and suppress fatigue long after most other people I know have packed it in.

(14) I thrive on deadlines. I like to work at maximum speed and will do anything to make a delivery.

(15) I'd rather have the admiration of my friends and coworkers than their affection.

(16) I rarely have any time to myself.

(17) I know I should exercise more and eat better, but I don't have time.

(18) When I'm under stress, I often have a cramp or a headache. Other times I've felt nauseated, dizzy, or faint, or broken out in a rash.

(19) I have trouble going to sleep. I can't turn off my mind after a busy day.

(20) I eat quickly, and I often eat and read at the same time. On workdays, I either eat at my desk or skip lunch altogether. Sometimes I get indigestion.

If you answered "yes" to these questions fewer than ten times, it's unlikely that stress is dominating your life at the moment. Read this book for tips on how to build hardiness against stress and prepare for the inevitable times when stressful events will threaten your health.

If you said "yes" between 11 and 15 times, you're likely a hard-driving individual who could benefit from a thorough read of this book. Adopt the prescriptive strategies to protect your health as well as improve your life.

If you answered "yes" more than 15 times—in particular, if you answered "yes" to questions 3, 8, 9, 10, 18, 19, or 20, read this book *now*. You need to understand the negative effect your lifestyle is having on your health (Part One), and start to practise the techniques in Part Two to make some immediate changes in how you handle stressful events. Then you need to work with the material in Parts Three and Four to make some long-term, healthy changes to the way you manage your life.

PART ONE

SO YOU THINK YOU KNOW ALL ABOUT STRESS...

"Let me assert my belief that the only thing that we have to fear is fear itself— nameless, unreasoning, unjustified terror that paralyses needed efforts to convert retreat into advance."

—F.D. ROOSEVELT, U.S. President
March 4, 1933, Inaugural Address

STRESS CAN BE A KILLER

As a family doctor who deals with stress-related conditions, I have treated hundreds of patients for disorders such as anxiety, depression, panic disorder, tension headache, migraine, abdominal pain, back pain, hypertension, diabetes, heart disease, and many more. These disorders, like almost all medical disorders, can be triggered or made worse by a person's reaction to what is going on in his or her life at the time.

We all know that our reaction to the stressors in our lives can bring on anxiety, depression, panic disorder, and the like. The idea that stress can also bring on heart attacks, strokes, and cancer is a bit more startling, but it's true.

This book is not about just giving you knowledge. Knowledge, as Emerson says, keeps no better than fish. I wrote this book to prompt you to take action to build a refined and integrated body and mind so that when you encounter difficulties in your life, you will not get sick. And I will give you tools for stress-proofing yourself so you can control how your body functions and reacts in tough times. These techniques will prevent your body from releasing some of the dangerous chemicals in reaction to stress, and thus prevent damage to your health as you face the challenges of modern life. But first, I need to show you exactly why it's so important to incorporate some of these practices into your life.

I'm going to tell you what usually happens to your body and brain when you have to face a stressful situation. The short story is that big changes are taking place, paving the way for illnesses of all sorts to take over unless you know how to eliminate what I call the "stress reaction," and you remember to put your knowledge into practice. I can't give you the magic words to ensure that bad (or even mildly unsettling) things won't happen to you—whether they come in the form of a critical boss, an angry child, a verbally abusive spouse, or just having too many things to do. But I can show you how to block the damaging physical and biochemical changes that usually accompany a stress reaction. These are the changes that weaken your heart, decrease your memory, diminish your immunity against colds, and generally set you up for a chronic illness.

In fact, I am going to show you how to stop a stress reaction in a few seconds. Life is really just a series of disturbing events and, if you are lucky, they will be interrupted by short periods of relative calm. It is crucial for you to learn how to stay grounded and balanced, and not allow the functioning of your body to be disturbed by the events of your life. Staying balanced, centered, and grounded is a great way to ward off a stress reaction when troubles arise.

Everyone is a stress management expert these days. Some tell us to think of stress as a friend to be entertained. They say that stress is what keeps you going. As a family doctor who treats real diseases, I want to impress upon you that a stress reaction is a profound and pernicious physiological reaction that not only keeps your body from functioning at its best, it can make you sick. It can even kill you. Don't think you are just basking in the glow and flow of a little adrenaline rush that is making you more productive and giving you an edge. The adrenaline and other chemicals associated with a stress reaction are doing their dirty work on your arteries. No wonder stress is linked to the leading causes of death in North America.

Hear this. When you allow a stress reaction to take over your system, you are setting a damaging physical reaction in motion. Learn how to defend yourself when stressors appear. Learn how to stop the negative reaction and shift gears.

When you find yourself in a stressful situation, the first thing to do is to stop your stress reaction. Then the negative effects on your nervous system and other parts of your body will not happen, or at least they will be minimized. If you are not able to stop the stress reaction, harmful chemicals will be secreted, your internal state will be affected in a negative way, and your health will begin to deteriorate.

STRESS REACTION PART 1:
FLIPPING THE SWITCH

You might have heard of the autonomic nervous system. This is the part of your nervous system that regulates the involuntary functions of your body—your heartbeat, digestion, breathing, kidney function, and so on. The autonomic nervous system is what keeps you ticking. If it's not working, you are a dead duck.

The autonomic nervous system is made up of two subsystems—the sympathetic nervous system and the parasympathetic nervous system—that govern how your internal organs, your blood vessels, and your glands function.

The sympathetic nervous system increases your heart rate, regulates the size of your blood vessels, and prepares your body for action—it puts you on "red alert." All your energy is focused on responding to what's happening; you're ready to either run or fight.

The parasympathetic nervous system does the opposite—it slows down your heart rate, dilates the blood vessels that take nourishment to your vital organs, and promotes processes such as digestion while it conserves energy. It is the system that cleanses and nourishes your body to strengthen and support you.

Your body can shift into the sympathetic mode to deal with the outside world or the parasympathetic mode to strengthen you on the inside. These two systems are usually in balance, but when you react to stress, the balance shifts to make the sympathetic system dominate.

When you are stressed about something, your hypothalamus—the master control organ of your body located in the base of your brain—gets the message that you're feeling under siege. It reacts by sending a message to your pituitary gland. From here impulses rush directly to your adrenal glands and other internal organs of your body to switch to your sympathetic system. All your energy is focused on taking action and the system that nourishes and supports you literally shuts down. How long do you think you can live this way and stay healthy?

It's Wednesday morning and Michelle has been up since 5 a.m., putting the finishing touches on a presentation she has to make to the management team at 9.

As she sees the time whizzing by, she takes a quick bath and carefully dresses in her expensive gray suit so she'll make the best impression at the meeting. As she hurries through breakfast, she spills coffee on herself.

By the time she is ready to leave the house, she is almost late. She jumps into her car and speeds off, but only until she manages to catch the first of many red lights on the way to her office.

With no time to spare, she is now getting upset and her blood pressure is spiraling upwards. There she is, sitting at her fourth red light with her shoulders hunched almost up to her ears with tension and perspiration beginning to stain her blouse.

As the light changes, a man in a red pickup truck pulls in front of her and proceeds to crawl along. Michelle tries to pass him, but there's too much traffic. She realizes that she is now late for what could be the presentation of her career, and her blood pressure goes up again. She feels exhausted.

She arrives at the office anxious and tense. As she gets to the boardroom, a coworker tells her that the 12 members of the management team (including her boss), plus a bank manager the boss decided to invite to hear her presentation, are already seated in the boardroom waiting for her. Michelle pictures them frowning, fidgeting, and checking their watches.

She grabs the doorknob and tries to let herself into the room. She cannot do it. Her muscles are weak, her palms are sweaty, her hands are trembling, her stomach is upset, her heart is beating like mad, and she feels a migraine coming on.

QUICK CHECKUP

How Do You Rate Your Stress Level?

1) Take a moment to rate the level of stress you feel right now from 1 to 10—where 10 is high stress. Give yourself a mark. Are you feeling more stressed or less stressed than you usually do? What would your usual mark be? How often do you feel overwhelmed and really nervous?

2) What are the causes of stress in your life right now? Write down three things that you know caused you, in the last week, to switch off the parasympathetic nervous system that nourishes you and keeps you healthy.

STRESS REACTION PART 2:
LIVING IN THE HORMONE RUSH

When the sympathetic nervous system is stimulated, it causes the release of adrenaline and cortisol—two key hormones that have a profound effect on the cells in your body. Take note of them. They govern your life and regulate your capacity to function. The physical effects of these hormones are what we associate with being stressed. When the daily hassles of life hit, these two hormones quickly break down sugars and any fat or protein they can access to make some quick energy to fuel the sympathetic nervous system in action.

These hormones break down stored fat as a last resort, by the way. Don't think that staying under stress will make you thin. Cortisol in particular will break down muscle tissue before it will go after your fat stores. Even worse, the stress will trigger cravings for fat and carbohydrates—to make sure you have enough energy to get you through this high-energy demand period—so you are more likely to *gain* weight as a result of being stressed.

So let's say you are under stress. Your heart is racing, your body is diverting energy from the processes of living, such as digesting your last meal and cleansing your body of toxins and viruses. Your energy is now focused on the process of defending yourself. Your muscles are tense and ready to help you fight or run away; your internal organs are hyperactive.

As if that is not enough, your brain is also flooded with cortisol. This cortisol changes the receptor site of some cells in your brain, leading to memory impairment. (Just when you need to be quick-witted, it's more likely you will forget important information because your capacity to remember facts is compromised.) And so, in general, you function far less effectively than you would without the excess levels of cortisol triggered by a stress reaction.

What's the point of this brief glimpse of a body at work when something upsetting happens? To make sure you know that the stress reaction is a serious physical response, and that these two hormones in particular are very powerful and produce severe changes in your body.

Ray left his office a little early on Friday afternoon, after the usual hectic week at the bank. He was looking forward to a relaxing weekend. As he pulled into his driveway, he saw his fifteen-year-old daughter coming home from school, holding hands with an older neighborhood boy who had been in trouble with the law. His daughter had been more quiet than usual during the past few weeks, but hadn't mentioned the boy. Ray immediately guessed that she'd been seeing him for some time. He felt a surge in his stomach and his breathing speeded up. His mind began racing as concerns for his daughter exploded, and he misjudged the space on the left side of the car and scraped it on the side of the garage. He got out of the car and headed for the house in a foul mood.

A little later, when his daughter came into the house and Ray asked her about the relationship, she accused him of spying on her. Then his daughter stormed out of the room, shouting, "Just leave me alone. It's none of your business!"

Ray was shocked by his daughter's outburst. He stood still, feeling his blood pressure rise and his heart pound.

QUICK CHECKUP

How Does Feeling Good Feel to You?

1) What's the lowest stress rating you'd ever give yourself? Picture yourself when you were functioning stress-free and relaxed.

2) Make a note of the scene. Visualize where you were, who you were with, the sounds, the surroundings—take yourself back there. Try to recapture the pleasant feeling in different parts of your body. Have you felt that way in the last month? In the past year?

STRESS REACTION PART 3:
ALL TENSED UP

When your body goes into stress reaction mode, one of the first parts of your brain to get the message is the premotor area—the area of the brain that controls the movement of your muscles. Your muscles are told to get ready for action—so they tighten up in response to what is going on, whether it's an argument with your spouse, insufficient funds in the bank, the rudeness of a client, or a pending legal action.

There are about 680 muscles in your body and when they are all told to contract in response to a perceived trouble that appears in your life, most of them do. This can produce neck pain, shoulder aches, or a headache. In fact, wherever there are muscles you can have an exaggerated and painful reaction to stress. And can you imagine the wasted energy expended while you're holding tension that is not going to be used? No wonder so many of us are worn out by the end of a challenging day.

What is more, each of us has a "favorite" place in our body that holds tension greedily and doesn't let go easily. That place will be particularly sensitive when your muscles respond to stress. Many office workers—secretaries, managers, executives, and accountants—find that their shoulder muscles are the primary location of a stress reaction, and it will be hard for them to let this tension go. Other people will suffer from neck pain and stiffness, especially at the end of a day's work. Some of us get severe lower back pain or pains in our legs; others can't get their legs to be still when they try to go to sleep. Severe chest pain can be another symptom.

These are your "hot spots"—those muscles that tense or

twitch on a regular basis when you feel stressed. Pay special attention to them and check them regularly. Consider the possibilities: your jaws, your back, your legs, or your shoulders—where are your shoulders right now? Up around your ears? Practise tension detection, especially around your hot spots, throughout the day. Make the muscle-tension sweep part of your pre-meeting or pre-appointment process; do it again after a long phone call. Train yourself to spot the onset of muscle tension and deal with it before it takes root.

Natasha was driving in her husband's new van to visit her mother on the other side of town. Taking extra precautions, she made the appropriate left turn; soon a driver from behind pulled up next to her, upset and giving her the finger. She could see he was shouting and swearing at her. She felt threatened and rattled by the gestures. The angry driver roared off, but by the time she got to her mother's place, Natasha had a severe cramp in her right hand from gripping the steering wheel and her neck was feeling stiff.

QUICK PRESCRIPTION 1

Cool Your "Hot Spots"

1) Identify your "hot spots" and pay special attention to those muscle groups.
2) Do a tension sweep of your body right now—which muscles are tense?
3) Take a deep breath and tense the part of your body where you feel the most tension.
4) Hold your breath and the tension for a few seconds and then release both. Repeat this breathe/tense/hold/release cycle three more times.

STRESS REACTION PART 4:
BOARDING THE EMOTIONAL ROLLER COASTER

When you are facing a stressful situation, your limbic system—the emotional center in your brain—is alerted and emotions such as fear, anger, frustration, guilt, depression, or self-doubt are produced. This is another powerful part of the stress reaction, and the emotions that are let loose can take over your mind and change your thinking. These emotions can direct your behavior and intensify your feelings of being stressed. And they are contagious when they are expressed—have you ever noticed a parade of negative emotions in the office when things are going badly? Your boss gets angry, then your coworker worries, your assistant may burst into tears, and you begin to feel overwhelmed. These are emotions caused by the stress reaction.

In stressful times, feelings of depression are common. When I see patients suffering from depression, their condition is often precipitated by some unpleasant event or disaster. Studies on stress and depression reveal that the more stressors you have to face, the more likely you are to suffer from depression. It is therefore wise to learn to deal with stressful events in addition to taking the medications that might be appropriate treatment for depression.

At any one time your emotions reflect the general way you are feeling that day or that hour, coupled with your immediate response to anything specific that might be going on at that minute. Most of us are not conscious of what we are feeling at any given moment, and our emotions tend to take root without our permission. The trick to staying off the emotional roller coaster is to live with an awareness of what you are experiencing, how that makes you feel, and how it's affecting your body. This awareness gives you some control, and you are relaxed to the degree to which you think you are in control of the events in your life.

The important point here is that you do have a choice about how you feel at any time. Don't take your emotions for granted, and don't think for a moment that you are a prisoner of them. Don't think they have to stay with you just because they appear. You can change your feelings if you are aware that you need to change them. Even in the most stressful situations, you can change the feelings that you experience almost as quickly as you can change your clothes. You can rise above the negative emotions that surge inside you when adversity strikes by taking action to change them. It all begins with living consciously.

To be mentally strong means you pay attention to your emotions and exercise control over the kinds of emotional reactions that you allow. The good news is that despite the sudden appearance and overwhelming power of the emotions triggered by a stressor, you are in charge. You are the author and director of the impulses that threaten to ruin your day. You are the producer and sustainer of the feelings that dominate your mind. These emotions are powerless if you decide not to let them dominate.

I feel so excited by the fact that no matter how disruptive the stressor might be, I always have the final word. I am the boss of my feelings. I find that what really matters is my resolve to choose positive emotions under all circumstances. For example, if someone criticizes me unjustly, I choose to fill my mind with the image of my little daughter clinging to me in her mysterious and loving way, and the negative feelings recede in the presence of the image and the strong positive feelings associated with it.

All of us have felt our limbic systems go to work, producing a potpourri of different, and often painful, emotions when we meet the unexpected. Your composure can be ruined if your limbic system is allowed to fill your mind with a variety of negative emotions when you are under stress. Remember that whatever you dwell on will expand in your life. This is true when you are under great stress. Learn to choose what is positive. Make this one of your mottoes.

The skill I want to help you develop as you read this book is called emotional redirection and in order for it to work, you must first cultivate emotional awareness. You can deal with your negative feelings only by first recognizing their presence.

Then you can decide that you will not allow the feeling, however potent it may seem, to dominate and ruin your day, your week, or your life. Only when you are emotionally aware can you begin to defuse negative emotions.

Develop a heightened awareness of how you are feeling at any given moment. Don't ever ignore the way you feel. Develop an emotion-detection habit. Pay attention to your inner state and know what kinds of emotions are there. Observe them without judgment. If you're feeling negative, don't get angry with yourself for feeling the way you do; simply note the emotion and how it's affecting you. If you are angry, take the opportunity to notice what your anger feels like. Where do you feel that emotion: in the pit of your stomach, in your chest, or in your head? Where does it hurt? What other physical effects does it have? Even if feelings of numbness or emptiness predominate, sink into them.

Ask yourself about the emotion: Where did this come from? Am I overtired? Is something else bothering me? Does this emotional response have all that much to do with what seems to have triggered it? Is it an emotion that will be useful or necessary when I deal with the situation?

Get to know your favorite positive emotions as well as the frequent negative ones so you will be aware of how you feel when you're feeling good. Knowing how you want to feel and being able to focus on creating (or recreating) those feelings are the core of emotional redirection. Once you've mastered this skill, no matter what is happening to you, if you want to be happy, you can make yourself happy as you shift your emotional state in that direction. You will be able to do the same if you want to feel confident or relaxed. For now, master the first step of emotional awareness.

It is Friday afternoon. Dave is confidently completing his work and clearing his desk so that he will be in time to pick up his partner and go for a special, relaxing dinner. Monday's "to-do" pile holds the things that can wait. He has just enough time to finish the work needed for Monday morning. Dave looks up from his desk and there she is—his boss—heading toward him with a serious look on her face and a thick report in her hand. She tells Dave she wants him to review it before he leaves.

He feels a sudden surge of anger, resentment, and hostility. He's thinking, "Why me? Why now?! I'll have to take work home..." His whole weekend is in danger of being ruined, not so much by his boss's request, but by his inability to master the emotions that flared after she made her request.

QUICK PRESCRIPTION 2

Rx

Develop Emotional Awareness

1) When you begin to feel stressed, notice the emotions that are taking over your mind.
2) Take a deep breath, and ask yourself where these emotions are coming from.
3) Ask yourself how you would prefer to feel.
4) Continue to breathe deeply and think about how you want to feel. Try to let that emotion expand and fill your body and mind.

STRESS DAMAGE: TAKING IT TO HEART AND MIND

We've looked at what happens during a stress reaction, and done a couple of exercises to start to head off that reaction. But what is the effect of that reaction? We are going to look at the key effects of the stress hormone adrenaline.

When adrenaline is released, what does it do besides give you a surge of energy and help you tighten your muscles? Any time you experience a shot of adrenaline, it raises the level of cholesterol in your blood, reduces the diameter of the blood vessels in your heart, brain, and kidneys, and does some damage to the inside of those and other blood vessels. This makes it easier for what are called plaques to form and deposit themselves on the walls of your blood vessels, setting the stage for closing the blood vessel altogether—and stopping the flow of blood to the area.

Adrenaline also causes the white blood cells to become sticky and to clump together and deposit on any plaques in the already constricting blood vessels in your heart and your brain. When the blockage reaches a certain level in your heart, you have a heart attack; when the blockage is in your brain, you have a stroke.

The point once again is that the stress reaction is significant and can go beyond muscle cramps and tension headaches to generate really bad consequences such as heart attacks, strokes, or kidney disease. These are the vital organs that the stress reaction tends to affect.

Every time you feel stressed, especially as a result of some situation or event, you should be aware of the dangerous reactions that are affecting your cardiovascular system as well as locking in muscle tension. The good news is that it is not your destiny to be constantly tense, overactive, and anxious as you ride an adrenaline wave. You can teach your body to relax, and that relaxation will stop the stress reaction.

Carmen was ushering her young family out the door in the usual morning scramble, when her youngest child suddenly exclaimed, "Mom, I forgot! Today is 'blue day' at school. I have to change my clothes!"

After arguing that it was too late to do such a thing, and then trying to find clean blue clothes, blue clothes that fit, or just any blue clothes, and one bout of tears (we won't say whose), Carmen and her family finally left fifteen minutes late, with parts of the house turned upside down.

Carmen was stressed out and so were the kids. As she hustled to catch up at work, Carmen could feel her pulse racing and it was mid-morning before she calmed down. For the rest of the day she felt a nagging little headache and a tight lump at the back of her neck; whenever she turned her head, she felt a knifelike pain.

QUICK PRESCRIPTION 3

Rx

Turn Off the Tap

1) Train yourself to relax; start by practising with your writing hand. With your hand free of objects, make a tight fist and then tense your arm up to your elbow.

2) Count to five and then let the tension go. Repeat the exercise three more times.

3) Wiggle your fingers and give your writing hand a little shake.

4) Breathe deeply and consciously as you exhale and feel all residual tension flowing out of your shoulder, arm, and hand. Keep breathing consciously and feeling your muscles relaxing more and more with each breath.

STRESS DAMAGE: NO ONE'S IMMUNE

When your body is in the throes of a stress reaction, you know which hormonal changes occur—adrenaline and cortisol in particular begin to dominate. When cortisol is secreted into your bloodstream during a stress reaction, this hormone causes your body's immune factors—such as cytokines (helper cells), and T-cells (natural killer cells) that usually survey and protect your body—to slow down on the job. Numerous studies have shown that stress causes an increase in symptoms of irritable bowel disease, arthritis, and other autoimmune disorders because of this decline. It also makes it easier for viruses, bacteria, and aberrant cells to attack. The net effect of stress on your body's cells is an increased susceptibility to illness or damage due to a weakening of your immune system.

Studies suggest that even after the stress reaction is over, the effect on your immune system will continue for a while. These negative effects can result in serious consequences. Some experts believe that abnormal cells, that are in some way related to the beginning of cancer, are constantly forming in our bodies and that they are kept in check and eliminated by the natural killer cells and other immune helpers. If your immune system is constantly compromised by stress reactions, it is easy to see how the risk of developing tumors and autoimmune disorders might increase.

If you think about a difficulty or a stressor that recurs in your life—such as a time at work or at home that is usually busy—try to remember what your health is like at the time and later. Remember year-end or Christmas? Or you may recall a time that was especially stressful: when you and your partner were at odds, when there was a lack of support from your supervisor, or when your company was in difficulty and jobs were at risk. Now note the times when you were feeling under the weather. When was the last time you were sick in bed, or had a low fever or a cold? Was there a relationship between your illness and the stressful times?

Take a moment and ask yourself which part of your body is likely to be at risk because of a recurring stressor. What might a stress reaction's effect be on your immune system?

In addition to your muscle spots, what other areas are most vulnerable when you're under stress? Your stomach? Your sinuses? Your colon? Your joints? Do you get indigestion, head colds, or diarrhea when you're feeling stressed? If you have a chronic illness, does it tend to flare up when you are under stress?

What illnesses are most common in your family? Have close relatives had heart attacks or strokes? Pay close attention to diseases that may run in your family and build your defense against stress in order to avoid those conditions.

Dan had been working night and day to get a new computer program up and running. His family had been very understanding and supportive while he was absent from them, and he promised them a special ski weekend away to celebrate his return to a more normal schedule. They did get away, but unfortunately, Dan got sick. While the rest of the family was out on the slopes and the trails, Dan was in bed with a cold and fever.

QUICK CHECKUP

When Do You Get Sick and Tired?

1) Review the past 12 months and make a note of when you were sick. What was happening at the time, or just before the bout of illness?

2) Note the common illnesses that seem to run in your family. Have you noticed any tendency to these types of illnesses yourself?

HOW DO YOU REACT TO STRESS?

In summary, when you encounter a stressor, the hypothalamus, the master control organ in your brain, immediately dispatches a message to the pituitary gland that controls almost all the other glands in your body—your thyroid, your adrenal gland, ovaries in women, and testes in men.

Because of the actions of the hypothalamus and the pituitary gland, two powerful hormones, adrenaline and cortisol, are released into your system in abundance. It is the release of these two hormones that can make a stress reaction such a devastating physical event. There are some easily recognizable physical changes that are usually produced by stressful situations if the process is allowed to run its course. How many of the following do you experience?

- Muscles all over your body tighten, especially in your "hot spots."
- Shallow, irregular breathing begins. This is a disturbance of the basic rhythm of life that will make it difficult for you to keep yourself calm.
- Negative emotions such as fear, anger, guilt, worry, and resentment, along with intrusive thoughts and negative self-statements, will suddenly pop into your head.
- Increased stimulation of your sympathetic nervous system leads to a loss of physiological balance. Your body shifts from parasympathetic (the system that nourishes your body) to sympathetic dominance as you gear up to fighting form.

- Blood is redirected to your larger muscles and your brain, and the tiny capillaries in your extremities are shut down. (When you're stressed, do you notice that your hands or feet get cold?) This shift in blood flow is associated with headaches.

- The muscles in your jaw and other areas in your face will likely tighten even more, until your face resembles an animal ready to go into battle.

These stress reactions are examples of how unpleasant events or circumstances can affect you physically and emotionally—and damage your health. The extent of any health-related damages that occur as a result of your stress reaction is determined by how many of the above reactions are triggered by the messages from your brain, and how long the state lasts.

If you change your physical and emotional reactions to a stressor, the health damage that stressful events can cause can be avoided—even though the circumstance itself will not change. It is important to remember that the mundane, irritating events of everyday life that can produce these stress reactions are the ones to watch out for. In times of real danger, you will need to be able to fight or take flight. But how often are you in danger? Consider how often the ringing of the phone or a loud noise will make you hold your breath. How many times in a single day does your boss or someone else look at you sternly, and you react by tightening your shoulders?

When you lose money in a vending machine, do you take a deep breath and relax, or do you hold your breath, tighten your facial muscles, and crank up the emotional turmoil by thinking negative thoughts? When you are sitting in traffic, do you allow anxious feelings to take control of your body and settle in for the rest of the day? When you are blamed for something you did not do, do you allow your anger and frustration to well up inside and shut down your parasympathetic nervous system that helps to protect you from disease?

The meeting downstairs starts in 15 minutes. You have your presentation ready; you just have to photocopy the back-up material to hand out. The phone rings and you take the call.

The customer's shipment was due yesterday and it hasn't arrived yet. The material is needed—they will run out in two days and they don't want to stop production. They have to get the material to the line and they have orders to fill. Your customer sounds stressed and is trying hard to pass the sense of urgency on to you. You promise to look into the situation right away and hang up.

You call production; they tell you the job was finished on time. You then place a quick call to shipping and leave a message asking them to trace the order. You make a note to follow up after the meeting, which starts in 9 minutes.

You go to the photocopier, which is available. You load your job and select the number of copies. The machine hums through two sets and then stops. The "paper jam" light comes on. How will your body react?

QUICK CHECKUP

How Was Your Week?

1) Keep a "stress diary" for a week and write down the events and how you reacted to them.

2) Take special note of areas of muscle tension, aches, digestive upsets, episodes of increased heart rate, and any tendency toward shallow breathing.

3) At the end of the week, count up the stress episodes and any physical changes you can associate with a stress reaction. How many times did it happen?

PART TWO

FROM STRESS REACTION TO CALM RESPONSE

"I have been through some terrible things—some of which actually happened."

—MARK TWAIN

WHAT IS THIS THING CALLED STRESS?

Now that I've told you about what's really happening to your body when you're under stress, I realize that you're probably feeling pretty stressed about it. Before you decide you have to quit your job, divorce your spouse, give away your kids, and move to a desert island, read on.

As a medical doctor, I have treated hundreds of patients with stress disorders. As a speaker, I have lectured to thousands of people on the subject of mastering the stress of life. In all my years of experience, the best definition of stress that I have ever heard is that ***stress is the response.*** Yes, stress is the response.

This means that the stress reaction and effects we've just been reviewing happen whenever you respond to the challenges of your life in a way that triggers the physical and emotional states we associate with being under stress. If you respond to the difficulties of your life in a way that ensures that the physical and emotional states that are consistent with the stress reaction are *not* produced, then you will not suffer from stress despite the presence of potentially stressful events in your life. Rather than reacting to events in an automatic way, consider responding to stressors in a thoughtful and deliberate way. You can train your physiology to shift gears and remain calm when troubles strike.

Whenever you are bombarded by hostile complaints from your customers, and you find yourself tense and upset, remember that stress is not the complaints, stress is your response.

Whenever your neck becomes rigid and painful after an argument with a family member, remember that stress is not your sibling, stress is your response.

If you have just been fired from a job you love, and your head begins to pound and you feel anxious, remember this definition: stress is your response to this disturbing trigger in your environment.

When you put yourself to a great deal of trouble to meet your boyfriend and he fails to show up, and anger and embarrassment overwhelm you to the point where you develop a stomachache, remember—stress is your response.

When the news that the stock you invested most of your money in has crashed to penny status sets off a migraine, remember—stress is your response.

When your boss is obnoxious and confrontational, and a dark cloud of depression begins to settle over your workstation, remember—stress is your response.

When your spouse snaps at you constantly, and anger, a desire for revenge, and depression begin to replace feelings of love and intimacy, remember—stress is your response.

When you discover that your son is in trouble and your daughter is going out with an unemployed drug addict, stress is your response.

You see, stress is the response you make to a situation that you have allowed to upset you. The event or situation that triggers stress is an event or situation. That's all. In most cases, it has no physical or emotional power over you. It can be an unpleasant situation—uncomfortable and even unacceptable—but no matter how unpalatable the situation may be, it cannot cause stress without your help. As Epictetus, the Greek Stoic philosopher, said long ago, man is distressed, not by events, but by his view of these events. This does not mean that you shouldn't do anything about the situation—it simply means that you can do something about it without being stressed.

The real key to the arrival of stress in your life is not what is happening, but the way you perceive the situation, and the physical, emotional, or behavioral responses that you make based on that perception. And that stress response will reduce your ability to deal with the situation in an effective way.

Don't think you are under stress because you are bombarded by troublesome events on all sides. If you stop to think about it, you will realize that everyone is in the same situation. You need much more than events to make you stressed.

Review the definition again: ***Stress is the response.*** But it is a certain type of response. It's a reaction that you have without giving it much thought. And you usually have this kind of reaction to a situation because it has surprised you or you perceive it as something beyond your ability to cope with or out of your control. In other words, perception precedes your reaction. You have to see the situation as more than just an event if it is going to make you feel stressed.

It is undeniable that in order to have stress, you have to have an activator or a stressor. But you also have to see the stressor as something threatening or unmanageable. You must see yourself as powerless or weak before the stressor. The moment you perceive a stressor as beyond your ability to cope with it, the negative physiological and biochemical reactions automatically begin in your body.

I want to get you thinking about your split-second perception because it is at the level of perception that you have the best chance to stop the effects of a stressor from damaging your health.

Your negative perception of any problem will work against you when you decide you are helpless or powerless, or that the event is so overwhelming that is it beyond your ability to affect it in any way. Either point of view will ensure an unhealthy response when troubles come your way. The reaction that happens inside your body when this negative perception reigns is the stress reaction. It is mostly the quality of perception that you bring to a stressor that will determine if the stress reaction will result and how big a reaction it will be.

If stress were expressed as an equation, it would look like this:

stressor + your negative perception = stress

It all happens so quickly that you are likely tempted to regard stress as an automatic phenomenon when troubles strike. This is not so. Look at the situation; it's the combination of the stressor and your perception of it that sets the course of the reaction. While you can't control the stressor, you *can* control your perception. Armed with this awareness, you will soon see many places where you can intervene and interrupt the process.

Mae and Gwen lived in the same building and often met in the elevator on their way to the garage in the mornings. On this day, they chatted on the way down and then made their way to their cars to go to their respective jobs. But something was wrong—as they walked to the area where their cars were parked, it was clear that vandals had been in the garage during the night. Broken glass crunched under their shoes. Members of the building security staff were making note of the damage and called out a warning to be careful. Neither of the women's cars had been spared—both arrived to see the windows smashed in on the driver's side and a mess in the interior.

Mae became very agitated. Stepping on the broken glass had set her teeth on edge. "My beautiful car! How could someone do this to me?! Look at the mess, the scratches—this is awful! If I could get my hands on those punks, I'd kill them," she seethed. "I don't have time to deal with this! I've got to get to work! I don't even know where I'd take the car to get it fixed. What am I going to do?!"

Gwen took a deep breath. "Yes, it is awful," she agreed. "This has happened to people I know. I guess it's our turn now. I am going to call my office and tell them I will be in later this morning. Then I'm going to call my insurance company, clean up the car, take it to the garage, and go into work. Would you like the name and number of the garage I go to?"

QUICK CHECKUP

What's Pushed Your Buttons Lately?

1) Even if you're keeping a stress diary, take a few moments to think about the number of times you've been deeply distressed, even lain awake at night worrying, or caught yourself doing a mental rant over something that came up in your life. Do you remember what triggered the anger and the stress?

2) What finally happened? Was it really more than you could manage?

3) Make a note of the last three things that had you worked up and talking to yourself (or others). Then write down what happened in the end.

PERCEPTION: THE GATEWAY TO STRESS . . . OR NOT

LET'S REVIEW OUR equation for stress: stressor + your negative perception = stress

From this equation, it is clear that no matter how powerful the stressor might be, it cannot provoke a stress response by itself. It needs your permission. And you give it permission when you choose to perceive the situation as threatening and unmanageable. As soon as your perception leads you to see the situation as having the upper hand, the stress reaction begins to create havoc in your system.

As we noted in the last section, there are two sides to this perception: your perception of yourself—"I can't handle this!"—and your perception of the event—"This isn't supposed to be happening!" Now try these perceptions instead: "I've dealt with something like this before and I can deal with this." And "This was totally unexpected, but how bad is it, really?"

The secret to preventing a stress reaction is to refuse to perceive the situation as beyond your ability to cope. This calls for you to defy the stressor by thinking and acting like a winner in the face of an unexpected or unfortunate situation. Take the point of view that you think a winner would adopt. Act like a winner and you will become a winner; the stressor will not harm you.

This positive attitude of mind is one that you must put on every day just as you put on your clothes, so that you develop the habit of always looking at potentially troublesome situations in light of your capabilities and your experience. Think like "The

Little Engine That Could"—this is why your parents kept reading that story to you. This attitude will change your perception of yourself for the better and help protect you from a damaging stress reaction.

You can (and should) work to change your perception of yourself and the situations you encounter if you're serious about fighting the effects of stress. You will have to do some work to earn the label that you are mentally strong. You don't just think it and say the words. Remember, nothing comes from nothing. If you don't take the time to change your perception of yourself and your troubles, if instead you tell yourself that you are too busy to practise the mental and physical techniques that will make you more positive and resilient, you will not master the stress in your life.

You see, the habit of always taking the negative or victim's point of view is actually programmed into your nervous system and it takes more than knowledge or casual efforts to make a real change. But you can change—don't just assume that you're going to live your life as a pessimist. From now on, see yourself as a person with power and internal fortitude.

What you need to do is take the time to regularly remind yourself about the adversities that you have overcome, and the strengths that you possess. You need to take yourself back to your most troubling times and learn from them. Do this reflection regularly, and you will gain confidence in your ability to cope with the stressors of life. You will strengthen your perception of yourself and start to become more resilient.

It takes will to show resilience in the face of challenges on a continuing basis. If you practise reinforcing your perception, you will be amazed at how much trouble you can withstand without feeling stressed.

Your perception is not fixed. It is malleable. Work on building your confidence by facing the stressor with a smile and telling yourself that you can cope. Work on adopting a point of view that will give you hope and power when you meet difficult situations. Work on accentuating the positive and eliminating the negative in your thoughts, intentions, attitudes, and actions. and think like a winner. Even though she had lost a battle, Serena is bound to win the war.

Serena discovered that a client she had spent a lot of time with had given her business to a rival company. The client had been one of Serena's more productive accounts and she had included the projected business in her quarterly sales forecasts. The news could have been a blow, but Serena didn't allow the message to derail her. Instead, she put the loss of the client into perspective—there's always client turnover, and she knew she was a good salesperson with a good product. She would now have more time to spend on bringing a couple of her newer clients along and pursuing some promising leads.

Since this former client had been pleasant to work with and had been a source of good business that had been appreciated, Serena called her former client to wish her well, and to let her know that she was always welcome to bring her business back. Serena used the conversation to do some research on her own business's services compared to those of the competitor.

Did Serena perceive the news as a disaster that would wreck her chances at a bonus in the next quarter? No, Serena assumed a position of strength and defused the stressor. She dared to act and think like a winner. Even though she had lost a battle, Serena is bound to win the war.

QUICK PRESCRIPTION 4

Rx

Perceive Yourself as a Winner

1) Take a few minutes to sit or lie down in solitude. Five minutes will suffice. Make sure you're in a comfortable position.

2) Tense your arms and legs and take a deep breath at the same time. Hold the tension and your breath for a few seconds and then exhale and release all the tension. Continue to breathe deeply and consciously and try to stay in touch with the rhythm of your breathing.

3) Recall as vividly as you can the worst predicament that you have overcome. Imagine the details—what you were wearing, the people around, the day, the surroundings, and exactly what happened. See yourself in the situation and recall what you did to overcome it.

4) Think about what you did that was most helpful. Think about the qualities you possess that made the successful resolution possible.

5) Promise yourself that when things go wrong, you will not panic, because your experience has told you that you have overcome obstacles before.

YOU CHOOSE YOUR RESPONSE

THE PERCEPTION THAT you are a person who can cope is a key factor in stopping the damaging reactions that happen in your body when you are facing stressful situations. Your perception of yourself is the main ingredient that will change the outcome of the stress equation to one that is healthier. Isn't it wonderful that positive perception is free and inexhaustible?

Whenever you are facing a stressor, no matter how devastating it appears to be, or how much things seem to be out of your control, remember that if you have control over nothing else, you have control over how you perceive the stressor and how you perceive yourself in the face of it. In fact, you have control over even more.

Whenever I face a predicament in which I seem to have little or no control, I always try to remember three powerful words that I learned from Brian Tracy, author of *Maximum Achievement*.

Take note of these three words and use them often. Every time something bad happens to you, every time your partner puts you down, every time you are passed over for a well-deserved promotion, use these three words to remind yourself that you still have some control. They have power, genius, and magic in them. The three words are ***I am responsible***.

I am responsible means that you are in charge. You are in control of what you do next. Resist the urge to feel helpless under stress; refuse to sit and be a victim. When you take charge, you are looking to thc future. You have already confirmed to yourself that you can cope. Now you are putting yourself in a position of power as you assume control. ***I am responsible*** means that you are responsible for how you perceive the situation, and how you respond to it. And the way you perceive and respond will influence the amount of stress you suffer as well as how things will turn out.

You are responsible for what happens to you when a stressor hits you, and you can direct your efforts toward ensuring that what comes next is not an explosion of muscle tension, negative emotions, and stress hormones on the loose. The future has yet to unfold and you can work to make it better than the past or the present. This, to a great extent, is under your control. Once you internalize the concept that you are in charge of choosing your response to the situation, all those stress reactions and their effects will not happen to you, even in the presence of the most provocative stressors.

So assume control over the situation. Even partial control. When you are not able to control all the elements of a stressful situation, do not give up the control you do have. You can always choose your point of view and how you respond.

Marla and her daughter Kelly had been at odds lately—over the usual mother–teenaged daughter issues about Kelly's appearance. Marla thought they had reached an agreement of sorts: when Kelly was going out with the family, she would dress as Marla thought was appropriate; when Kelly was going out with her friends, she could dress more as she pleased.

Early Saturday afternoon, the family was getting ready to go to a wedding. Marla's husband was out warming up the car and everyone else was ready at the door before Kelly made her entrance. It was spectacular: she was dressed in her favorite black, including her Doc Martens. Even her nail polish and her lipstick were black. She had, however, spent the morning dying her hair blue, and her midriff was visible in the gap between her top and her skirt.

Marla stopped breathing for a moment and closed her eyes. She had been looking forward to this party. She and her husband were good friends of the groom's parents. She asked herself, "Will I, a grown-up... who once owned some outfits that distressed my *mother... let a common act of teenage rebellion ruin a party with my husband and some good friends?"*

Marla stifled her impulse to yell at Kelly in front of the younger kids who were nervously eyeing their mother. It was too late to send Kelly back to change, and she was absolutely not going to be allowed to stay home by herself on Saturday afternoon and evening. Marla wondered what people would think of her and her husband. Wryly, she realized people would think that she and Bill were parents of a typical teenaged girl. Marla took a deep breath and forced herself to say, "Ah, you're ready. Let's go."

As the family headed to the car, Marla could see her husband's eyes widen when he caught sight of his eldest daughter, and she shook her head to warn him to avoid an outburst.

QUICK PRESCRIPTION 5

Block a Stress Reaction

1) Take a deep breath in response to any stressful situation and exhale slowly, extending your out-breath. If, in the face of stressful events, you alter your breathing by deliberately taking slow, deep breaths, you will begin to alter your reaction to the stressors in your life.

2) Make that deep breath your reminder to examine your perception of the situation. You know you're a competent individual. Have you done this before? Is this really a disaster?

3) Remind yourself who is running your life: you are responsible for what happens next. Tell yourself that you are in charge and you can cope.

4) Think about the best ways to respond to the stressor—choose the one that helps the situation and keeps you calm.

DEFUSING STRESS: STEP-BY-STEP

THE CENTRAL MESSAGE that I want to convey is that no matter where you are in your life—no matter how financially destitute you might be, how hostile your work environment might be, how unwell you might be, or how disturbing your relationships at home may be—you can master stress and avoid the damage it can do to your health.

You will eventually learn to become more resilient in the face of stress, but first you need to stop the unnecessary stress you are suffering due to the little things—those mosquitoes that assail you on a daily basis. I am going to give you a six-point formula that will enable you not only to deal with a distressing situation without distress, but to emerge feeling much better and stronger than you felt before the encounter. No matter what the size of the troubles you are facing right now, I want you to adopt the view that those troubles don't have to trigger the stress reaction and compromise your health as well.

As I've outlined, first you must resolve that whenever you find yourself in an unpleasant situation, you are going to perceive it as something you can deal with. Then you are going to choose to take responsibility for your response and stop any damaging reaction in its tracks.

Now I'm going to show you how to do just that. You're going to arrest the stressor so to speak, and walk away from it as a conquering hero. If you interrupt the stressor, you will defuse its potential impact on you; you will be healthier and in a better position to deal with it.

Use this six-point formula to take control of yourself and your response when you are confronted by a stressor, whether it comes in the form of an accusation, road rage, aging parents, demanding teens, an angry spouse, or a visit to the dentist.

As you go about your daily business, remember that you will probably be facing potentially stressful events or find yourself in painful predicaments from time to time. Plan to **A.R.R.E.S.T.** the stressor. Memorize this six-point formula, and practise using it every day to deal with the stressors in your life.

A.R.R.E.S.T. is an action formula that stands for:

1) **A**nticipate and plan.
2) **R**estrict the influence of the stressor.
3) **R**espond calmly, don't just react.
4) **E**stablish control over your body.
5) **S**low down and seek your inner strength.
6) **T**hink optimistically about your goals.

Whether you are already in the middle of a stressful situation or you are likely to be hit by a stressor—and we all are—you can use the six-point formula to stop a stressor from causing a harmful stress reaction.

Allan is a busy IT supervisor for a medium-sized company. He and his team have just successfully completed a changeover to a new server and a new operating system. It's been a busy time and not without its challenges, but the first day fully on the new server and system has been relatively problem free. He's just thinking that he should take his team out for a little post-work celebration when one of his staff arrives at his office door.

"Something's wrong, Allan," she says. "I'm watching the end-of-day procedure and I think there's an error." She looks worried. "The screen has turned blue."

"Ah," Allan says as he gets up to follow her. "That would be what we call the 'Blue Screen of Death'."

QUICK PRESCRIPTION 6

Rx

Put Stress Under A.R.R.E.S.T.

1) Remind yourself you're someone who can handle what's coming.

2) Decide to take responsibility for what happens to you when a stressor pops up.

3) Review the **A.R.R.E.S.T.** formula and employ the steps that apply to your situation.

1. ANTICIPATE AND PLAN

Anticipate what stressors are likely to come your way and be ready for them. One of the elements that makes a situation distressing is surprise—it's the unexpected that makes you feel out of control.

Since today's business environment is characterized by sudden change and unexpected challenges, you need to adopt a "what if?" attitude: What if my boss chews me out for this report? I will take some deep, relaxing breaths, and then I will deal with the problem with a can-do attitude.

I believe that most stressors are predictable. If you stop and think for a while, you will realize how great a prophet you really are. You can usually predict a number of the things that are going to happen to you and where the potential for a stress reaction will lie.

Take a few minutes at the start of every day or each week to think about what's on the calendar—both regular and special events, appointments, or meetings. If you bring each day into focus, you will find that you have the ability to predict most of the things that will happen. Many situations that could catch you by surprise can be predicted. Take the time to think about what's coming up. You can remove the element of surprise by predicting a stressor and then planning how you will defuse or eliminate it. At the very least, you won't feel out of control because you had an idea of what was coming.

If you want to know what stressors are likely to affect you, you can use six simple questions and apply them to your life at the beginning of every day or week. Journalists rely on them to get a story straight and they will serve your needs as well. Just sit down and review upcoming events to uncover the hidden stressors that are likely to strike you with these six questions in mind: Who? What? When? Where? Why? and How? Or use them any time you're about to tackle a difficult task.

With the help of these questions, you can prepare yourself and take the sting out of many potential stressors that could go on to produce a stress reaction and ultimately damage your health.

For instance, in the coming week:

- Do you have any work-related deadlines, special meetings, or presentations?
- Do you have an appointment with an unpleasant client or customer?
- If you have kids, do they have projects due (or exams), practices, or appointments?
- If you have a partner, what's on his or her schedule?
- Does your boss or work team have to do any major reports or clear a big backlog?
- Do any of your extended family members have medical tests or concerns?
- Are you going to have to deal with an unpleasant situation you've been avoiding?
- Are there any household-related projects underway or about to begin?
- Is it just a very busy week coming up for everyone?

The point is that you can predict to a great extent the stressors that will bombard you, but if you're like most of us, you tend to ignore this power. Instead you end up like a victim being overtaken by difficulties that you could have been prepared for, if only you had made use of the power of anticipation. This is mindless behavior. Stop acting like an unsuspecting victim.

Consider your usual times of stress and plan to eliminate them. Always rattled in the morning? Try giving yourself more time. Always running behind at month end? Delegate or cut down on the "to-do" list. To anticipate a stressor means that you are going to deal with it as much as possible in advance. If you are under continual stress, play a game with yourself. Interrupt the pattern of stress by using your powers of prediction. Become a prophet and see how accurately you can predict when the stress episodes will happen. You may not be able to predict the exact details of the events, but you will be ready—with a calm mind and a relaxed body—for something. You will find that when you predict how, when, where, or why a stressor will strike, you have already softened the blow.

Simone reviewed her appointment calendar for the week and noticed that she had a Wednesday meeting with a particularly difficult client at 2 p.m. This client was never satisfied, no matter how prompt and flawless the service was. Her team had done the latest job as promised. The client was coming in to challenge the bill and announced that he was bringing along a detailed list of the shortcomings of their work.

Simone knew it could be a stressful session and made some advance plans to deal with the situation. She would pull the reports on the job, and talk to colleagues in production. She would get her notes on how the competition priced their work. But more than that, she would bring (and eat) an orange and drink lots of water before the meeting so she would be alert and relaxed for the encounter. She would make a note to remind herself to breathe fully and calmly during the meeting.

Simone also planned to get to the meeting a bit early and spend some time just breathing deeply and relaxing her muscles so she would be ready for any other stressors that might crop up during the session.

She smiled to herself, thinking it was an elaborate set of plans to deal with one cranky customer, but figured the mid-week strategy would be well worth it. If she didn't let that meeting get to her, she knew she'd have a good chance of functioning at her best for the rest of the week.

QUICK PRESCRIPTION 7

Head Stress Off at the Pass

1) Take an inventory of your crunch times. Ask your partner or a close friend what time of the year, month, week, or day they've noticed that you are usually rattled or in a panic. Get outside feedback about the times others think you suffer from stress.

2) Take note of the times in the calendar or the day when you are vulnerable and plan tactics to overcome the challenges.

3) Visualize yourself going through a stressful situation in a calm and relaxed manner. Then make the plans necessary to achieve it.

2. RESTRICT THE INFLUENCE OF THE STRESSOR

Minor stressors such as wondering whether you used the right word, the morning rush, heavy traffic, an important meeting, or a lovers' quarrel are the kinds of disturbances that produce needless malfunctions in your body and mind over time. These ordinary bites of life are no more than that—are you going to let them ruin your health? Not if you look at the big picture.

As you put a current stressor into the bigger context of what's happening in your life, you will realize that even though this stressor is happening in a small part of your life, it has the potential to spread its influence to areas that have nothing to do with it. It's important to quarantine the stressor—restrict its influence.

Have you ever taken a bad day at work home with you and made it a bad day for everyone else there? Even the cat went into hiding when she could have been giving you some comfort. What you have done is allow a single stressor to stir up negative emotions and upset the balance between your sympathetic and parasympathetic systems. Then you've permitted these negative feelings to affect all the other aspects of your life—even your most treasured relationships. You've given one negative event the power to influence you and everyone you come into contact with. This is a very common mistake.

One of the markers of stress in a family or at work is a general deterioration of relationships. This is why it is so important for you to resolve that at the first sign of stress, you are going to restrict its influence by bolstering all the important relationships in your life. When troubles strike, tell yourself that the time to be happy, cheerful, and loving is now.

Whatever you do, don't become a stressor yourself. Don't feel you have to spread your stressor's influence. This doesn't mean that you can't talk about your bad day (or your bad boss or evil client)—by all means share the events. But remember—they're just events. This means that you must put them in their place. Once you've talked about your boss's unfair criticism, ask your spouse about his or her day and plan to do something together—perhaps dinner or a movie. Focus on your love for each other. Once you've shared your day's difficulties with the computer system with your son, make plans to take in that game you've been promising him for so long. Their support in return will ensure that your relationships improve rather than deteriorate because of your difficulties. Be so busy cultivating good feelings around you that the negative effects of the stressor will be small in comparison.

The rule is: don't allow a problem at work to spoil your relationships at home; don't allow a problem at home to ruin your relationships at work. In fact, do the opposite: as soon as you realize that a stressor is on the loose in one area of your life, decide immediately to preserve and even strengthen other areas of your life. The real point here is to surround yourself with so much love and support that the negative influences of a stressor cannot penetrate into the deep places and rob you of the joys of your life.

Paul was 33, single, and off for a game of golf with his closest buddy. When Paul arrived, his buddy introduced his sister—Paul hadn't seen her in years. She was visiting from San Francisco and wanted to come along. That was fine with Paul. From the moment he laid eyes on her, he was captivated, and he really wanted to impress her, especially with his skills on the course.

As the day progressed, she was scoring just over par, while Paul was struggling. By the end of the day, Paul had been in three sand traps and triple-bogied once, while she had two birdies on her scorecard. Paul was embarrassed and irritable. He had a minor stressor on his hands. He could hear anger and resentment gently knocking at the door of his heart, wanting to come in and stay. Without thinking about it, he obliged. He became sulky. His answers to questions were curt. His face dropped its usual smile and energy. It wasn't a pleasant afternoon.

By the time Paul arrived home, he realized that not only had he behaved badly in front of someone he had wanted to impress, now his relationship with his buddy was strained, and that made him angry with himself.

After a brief exchange about housekeeping standards with his roommate, his roommate said, "Man, are you in a bad mood. Don't take whatever's bugging you out on me!" And when his mother called, he was unpleasant with her. Paul was on the way to allowing all his relationships to deteriorate because of a rather mundane affront to his pride.

QUICK PRESCRIPTION 8

Rein in Your Stressors

1) When a difficult situation arises, ask yourself if it's worth making yourself ill or punishing your loved ones.
2) Take steps to strengthen the important relationships in your life. Call a sibling or your partner and remind them that you love them.
3) Think about one thing you can do to strengthen your relationships and restrict the influence of the stressors in your life. Then do it.
4) Take the time to be supportive of your friends and family, and when stressors invade your territory, remind yourself, over and over again, "the time to be happy is now."

3. RESPOND CALMLY—DON'T JUST REACT

The difference between those who become stressed when confronted by a stressor and those who don't is the ability to remain calm both in the way you behave as well as in the cells and organs of your body. Beware of sudden emotional arousal. Energy is diverted from the brain and is wasted holding useless tension or nurturing negative emotions.

This third step in preventing the stress reaction when stressors invade your life is to train yourself to respond calmly to the stressor instead of reacting emotionally to it. When a stressful situation triggers you immediately into action, you are a victim and your body goes into the stress mode, pumping hormones and weakening your immune system. When you respond calmly instead, you retain that all-important balance in your body and you can take time to choose your way of meeting the difficulty as you breathe deeply and let tension drain out of your muscles.

One way to remain calm is to respond impersonally—get the facts about the situation, the bare facts. Deal only with the facts, not your feelings. Ask yourself what exactly has happened. Do a reality check. Don't make things worse than they are. Remember perception: it may seem like a catastrophe, but is it really? Have you faced a similar predicament before?

When you worked on your perception of yourself earlier, you were advised to visualize the worst thing that you have overcome. Now, do an assessment. How does this situation compare? If it isn't as bad, you can manage. If it's a bit worse, you can manage that as well. Recognize that you have the capacity to cope, and ascertain what needs to be done. Above all, don't take the situation personally. Everything doesn't just happen to you. It only seems that way at the moment.

Phil had his kids out for the day and was enjoying some fun on the playground in beautiful weather. He was rolling a ball to his youngest while the two older children climbed on equipment a few feet away. Then he heard what every parent dreads—a little yell, a thud, and his daughter crying and screaming. He looked at the equipment area and saw his older son's face quickly becoming covered in blood. His heart stopped for a second. Three small children, one hurt (how badly?), and one dad to deal with it all.

Phil took a deep breath and began to move. Scooping up Jake, he headed for his older son. He put Jake down beside Meghan and said as calmly as he could, "OK, guys, this looks pretty scary. I need to see what's happened to Andy. Meghan, hold onto Jake. You two stay put, please. Close your eyes if you don't want to look. Take some deep breaths, everybody. In: one, two; out: one, two. Andy, can you talk to Daddy?"

Phil remembered other parents' stories about how much head wounds bleed and was determined not to panic or alarm the kids any more than they already were. He reminded himself that he hadn't fainted when the kids were born; he should be able to deal with this. He put his hand on Andy to reassure him and got his brain in gear. He tried to recall some old first aid training: what's next? Check Andy's breathing—it's OK. Is he conscious? Yes, he's crying. Try to slow the bleeding—with what?

"Jake, Daddy needs to borrow your shirt to help Andy. Let's do another breath. In: one, two; out: one, two. Meg, you count the breaths for us, OK?" He gently mopped up Andy's face and head until he found the cut—long, but nothing was flapping—and put some steady pressure on it to stop the bleeding. Now that he had an idea of how serious the problem was, he could decide what to do.

"Andy's going to be OK, but we have to go to the clinic, guys."

QUICK PRESCRIPTION 9

Rx

Calmly Handle a Stressful Situation

1) Immediately tense your body and take a deep breath. Then relax as you breathe out. Breathe slowly, evenly, and deliberately. Continue to do this.

2) Banish any negative emotions such as anger, hostility, resentment, revenge, fear, sadness, and self-doubt that your limbic system may be dishing out. Tell them "no." Allow only the best and brightest feelings to remain.

3) Let your mind recall similar situations that you've been through. How did you respond then? What did you learn from that time? What skills and experience can you apply now?

4) Prepare your response based on the facts—not feelings, but facts. Continue to breathe deeply. Do you know what to do? If not, who does? Do you have to do something right now? If not, take some time to find out what others have done before you choose your course of action.

5) Once an appropriate course of action becomes apparent—even if it is summoning assistance—get busy doing it. Stress recedes in the presence of positive, meaningful action.

4. ESTABLISH CONTROL OVER YOUR BODY'S REACTIONS

When you find yourself in a stressful situation, immediately think control. Once you've taken steps to remain calm mentally and assess the situation, make sure you take control of your physical reactions. You want to stop any runaway hormones and muscle tension as soon as possible.

While it is unlikely that you can gain control over all aspects of a situation, remember that you always have control over yourself. You are responsible. Even if your body has begun to go on red alert, you can take charge and change the process. Once you establish this control, you may well see other aspects of the situation, no matter how small, that you can also influence in a positive manner.

Get in the habit of establishing control over your internal environment (mental and physical) as soon as you are affected by any difficulty. Recognize where all else ends and your sacred territory begins. This holy ground should be the primary target as far as establishing control goes.

The next prescription is one that you should practise daily. If you do, you will train your mind and your body in a pattern that will become second nature and easy to initiate when a stressor enters your world. This is known as autogenic training—a series of mental exercises in a certain sequence used to establish physiological and emotional balance.

As soon as something challenging happens, first take a deep breath and tense and relax your muscles to induce physiological harmony and to give yourself time to step back from the stressor and consider how to respond. A technique as simple as taking a deep, conscious breath, and relaxing your arms and legs can go a long way in keeping stress at bay.

As he waited off-stage before his first speech at a symposium, Mike did a quick tension sweep—to take his mind off his nervousness—and sure enough, the usual trouble spots were tightening up.

"Oh great," he thought. "First my shoulders will rise up and turn into cement. Then my hands will shake. I'll be hunched over the lectern like Quasimodo, clutching it to keep my hands still. They'll have to pry me off it by the time I'm finished. This is going to be the most uncomfortable hour of my life!"

He only had a few minutes—he took a deep breath. Then he told himself, "You know this subject—you were invited because you're an expert. Your presentation is good. Even your wife said so, and when something's not good, she doesn't hesitate to let you know."

With that he took a deep, slow breath and tensed his muscles. Then he relaxed them. He concentrated on his arms and legs starting to feel heavy and warm. Then the last step—the one that was the challenging one—he smiled. He was well into conscious breathing and relaxing his muscles when he heard his name announced and he walked out onto the stage feeling relaxed and confident.

QUICK PRESCRIPTION 10

Train Your Muscles to Relax

1) Take a deep breath and tense all the muscles in your body. Let your breath out slowly and let the muscle tension go at the same time.

2) Become aware of your arms and legs. Tell yourself that they are becoming heavy and warm. And as you breathe in, feel your arms and legs as they touch the chair, the couch, or as your feet touch the floor. As you breathe out, feel heaviness and warmth moving into your arms and legs and say to yourself, "My arms and legs are heavy and warm. Warmth is flowing into my arms and into my legs." Say this to yourself every time you breathe out. Focus and feel it happen.

3) Breathe with awareness—keep your breathing deep, slow, and even. Clear your mind by focusing on the warm and relaxing transformation as it takes place in your body. Pay attention to the quieting response as you do the exercise. Keep on breathing deeply and evenly. Notice the incredible feeling of physical harmony settling into your body.

4) Smile—inwardly and outwardly. Smiling can change the chemistry in your body in a very positive way. Smile with every muscle in your body and think a positive thought—tell yourself that you are a winner.

5. SLOW DOWN AND SEEK YOUR INNER STRENGTH

Whenever we find ourselves in stressful situations, we usually throw ourselves into a frenzy of activities to try to catch up or get rid of the stressful situation in some way. We use that muscle tension and adrenaline to spring into action once the first idea of what to do pops into our heads. We work at a frantic pace and we lose control of ourselves and our purpose.

The next time you find yourself in a stressful situation, do the opposite: *slow down your movements*. Pay attention to your breathing and then to how your hands or feet are moving. Observe your movements without judgment. Just notice what is going on, and then slow down your movements.

Use your relaxation training to calm yourself emotionally and physically. Often that will be enough to get you through a situation, but sometimes the stressor will be a prolonged one. You may feel like your soul is being tried and you will need to find deeper, inner resources to get you through.

The truth is that you have what it takes to overcome the stressors in your life. You are a gifted individual with a great deal of inner strength, but your inner strength has to be accessible. It also has to be nurtured on a continuing basis.

As you slow down and let go of muscle tension, your attention tends to naturally turn inward. And this is where your power lies. As you act from this deep place, your actions become more meaningful as you bring more power to bear from within. The truth is that when troubles strike, even good friends and close family cannot bail you out. They can offer emotional support, but they cannot rescue you. Don't wish or pray for someone to ride out of the wilderness on a white horse and make the bad situations disappear. That isn't going to happen. Instead, ask that the resources you already have will be used wisely and to good effect. This takes some reflection.

When you are confronted by daunting stressors, ask yourself, "What is the source of my inner strength?" You will often find the source by stepping back from what is overwhelming you and going back to a relationship that sustains you, or to the philosophies and principles that you learned as a child, or to some spiritual practice that you have allowed to slip from your daily routine.

When the problem is long-term, it is time to stop and gather strength. What is the source of your strength? Where do you reach for the power to overcome adversities? If you can't answer that question right now, in Part Three I'll help you work to discover it, and eventually the answer will appear.

Remember that you are more than your body, more than your mind, and more than your emotions. You are more than the total of all these. You can have access to deeper powers that can secure the kind of life that is slipping away from you. So a good strategy in times of stress is to find your inner strength. Knowing where you can get such help is one of the biggest secrets of a successful life.

Practise the technique of letting go prescribed below, called "soft eyes," to enhance your sense of control by intensifying your inner focus. The technique will help you generate a feeling of wholeness and you will be able to act with more power and awareness. It is a way of allowing your inner being to unfold and your inner power to surface.

Louise and Katherine had been friends since grade school and still got together once in a while. They placed their orders for dinner and then Katherine asked the big question: "How's work? How's your monster coworker?"

"Ah! The same. The same, only more so. She's got no authority in my area—we report to the same boss, but our work is separate—but she seems to be able to second-guess what my team is doing and talk about me behind my back. Now she's started a rumor that I'm so stressed she thinks I might have a breakdown. If I do, she's the one who will drive me to it! She's always finding a crisis—or inventing one—and then stepping in to save the day, while I just plod on, doing my job. She knows how to work the system—now she's finagling a trip to a European conference for herself. Why can't they see what she's like?"

"Are you going to quit?"

"I've thought and thought about it, but the work is satisfying and there aren't many positions like it these days. I can't just march out and get another job. And I can't just quit, either. I've got too many financial obligations. And that cow sure isn't going to leave… Listen to me talk! I'm becoming a person I don't even like. Complaining all the time, ranting, and back-biting. This isn't me. This isn't who I was raised to be. I'm an effective, competent, decent person … at least I was."

"Yeah, you were. You probably still are deep down. So how were you raised?"

"Oh, you know—turn the other cheek; do unto others; if you can't say something nice, don't say anything at all. All that stuff my grandmother used to lay on me."

"Sounds positively biblical."

"Well, people have been following that advice for generations. Maybe I should try it, or at least take some time to think about why it's supposed to work. Maybe I can talk to my aunt. She's the churchgoer in the family and come to think of it, she's one of the calmer members. I can't change the Monster, so I'm going to have to find some way to change myself so I can go back to being who I was."

QUICK PRESCRIPTION 11

Rx

Go Inside to Find Your Strength

1) Look in the distance in front of you for a few moments. Looking out a window or at the other end of the room will be enough. Open your eyes, but look at nothing in particular. Just let your eyes take in everything in general; your attention will start to connect to the center of your being.

2) Once you've softened your focus, begin to breathe from your center. Put your left hand on your abdomen, an inch or two below your navel to locate your center. As you hold your hand on this spot, feel your belly rise as you breathe in and fall as you breathe out. As you continue to breathe, you will begin to feel more centered and grounded, more balanced, more able to deal with the pressures around you, because of the power that you will have accessed inside you.

6. THINK OPTIMISTICALLY ABOUT YOUR GOALS

The last step in the formula for taming a stressor is to use your goals and dreams to defy it. Look beyond the negativity of the moment and keep your thoughts on creating a blueprint for a better life. When we are stressed, we tend to lose sight of what's possible and what's important and think in self-sabotaging, victimizing terms.

When you are in the throes of a stressful situation, you can be so busy reacting that you often fail to connect to the thinking part of your brain. You fail in those moments to realize the tremendous power that thoughts have over your life and your health, and you ignore a great source of available help, the kind of help that can change the course of your life. When faced with a stressor, search for any angle that will give you a way to exert some positive influence. Look for ways to find advantage in the situation if you can. And think about the situation in terms of your immediate and long-term goals.

Your goals are magical things. Even in the presence of a project going awry, a troubled relationship, a career seeming to go off-track, or money problems, if your thoughts are positive and focused on your goals, your life will tend to be positive. You will be able to move in the direction of what matters to you. This is the great reward for acquiring the discipline to remember your goals—what is truly important—in the midst of those clouds of buzzing mosquitoes.

When you concentrate on thoughts of your goals, your attitude and your actions tend to fall in line with your thoughts. Your physical and biochemical reactions shift to match the activities or behaviors that you think about.

When you're confronted by a stressor, if all you can think

about is disaster, your physiology takes on the characteristics of a person who is expecting disaster, you will feel and react like someone in the midst of disaster, and disaster is what you will likely encounter.

It seems natural to keep your thoughts on what you *don't* want to have happen when you are under stress. That is why it is important to train yourself to adopt the habit of keeping your thoughts on what you *do* want to have happen. Defy circumstances with the power of your thoughts—focus on the positive actions and outcomes that are consistent with your goals. Practise reminding yourself of your goals, even in bad situations. Keep your mind on what you want to achieve and who you want to be. Don't let any stressful situation change that.

Let a stressor be a cue to engage in positive thoughts that take you in the direction you want to go in. Whatever you think about will expand to influence your intention, attitude, and activities, which determine your destiny. This is not a big secret. Golfers will tell you to look at the flag in the hole, not the sand trap. Paddlers will tell you to look at the way through the rapids, not the boiling water on either side. Mountain climbers will tell you to look at the way up to the peaks, not the drop below you.

Remember we talked about life being nothing but a string of stressors? Well if this is so, it is crucial for you to learn how to control your thoughts and keep them focused on positive outcomes. Negative events can easily spark negative thoughts; negative thoughts can lead you to negative outcomes. By thinking positive thoughts, you will have your thinking aligned to support your goals. When there is a setback you will find it much easier to use the power of positive thought to propel you through the day's difficulties and closer to your goal. Defuse the power of a stressor with optimistic thoughts, attitudes, and intentions.

Don't abandon your goals and your principles when you are under stress.

Earl Nightingale is credited with the statement "You become what you think about." Since you are always facing stressors, make sure that you know what you want to become and think about that when troubles strike. If you don't keep your goals in mind, it will take too much energy to bring them to the fore when challenges come up. The time to become forward thinking and establish the significance of your goals is now.

Jackie had always dreamed of having a successful business of her own. Now she was a small business owner, but she was in severe financial trouble. Her customers couldn't pay their bills, and her suppliers were hounding her for their money. The bank could not extend her line of credit. She was caught in the middle and in danger of being wiped out.

Her only goal became finding a way to turn things around and getting her dream business back on track. Jackie focused on reversing her predicament. She didn't go into long laments. She didn't blame her customers, who had non-paying customers of their own. Nor did she scare herself daily with the prospect of what it would be like if she had to declare bankruptcy.

She thought continually about a positive outcome and kept the image of her goal in her mind. Then she made a plan that would get her back to solvency and was relentless in her pursuit of it. She worked with her banker, her suppliers, and her customers. She analyzed how she had gotten into this precarious state and made changes in her business. In a surprisingly short time, she was more successful than she had been before the cash squeeze struck. Her thinking paved the way for positive actions that got her back on track to her dream.

QUICK PRESCRIPTION 12

Keep Your Eyes on Your Goals

1) Focus on your immediate goals as well as your long-term ones—your magnificent obsession—and see how you can use the stressful situation to advance toward your goals. Focus on the mental image of a great future for yourself and for those around you.

2) Set out concrete, achievable steps that will lead you from the stressful situation to your goals.

DON'T HESITATE TO DEPLOY YOUR RESOURCES

WHEN YOU COME face to face with a stressful situation, immediately ask yourself what resources you have at your disposal to deal with the stressor. Use what you have to prevent the stressor from causing you stress and ruining your health.

Think of it like this: as you move to arrest the stressor, you have an arsenal at your disposal—you are not a victim. Don't be afraid to use every means at your disposal to keep a stress reaction from damaging your body and mind. Remember that once you feel stressed, your most precious gift, your health, is put at risk. You owe it to yourself and those around you to do everything in your power to stop stress from invading your sacred terrain.

You have six key resources that you can use to prevent stressors from producing an unhealthy stress reaction. They are:

- your brain
- your energy
- your time
- your money
- other people
- your spiritual connection

As you work to change your perception of yourself and situations, and to stop stressors from having a negative impact on you, you will be using your brain, energy, and time. In the short term, take the time to use your brain and your energy to forecast what is likely to happen and figure out a path of escape or a way to cope. Do this in advance of upcoming stressful situations. Just as you plan for profits using a marketing strategy, plan for health and happiness using a stress-reduction strategy.

In the longer term, you can use your energy and time to attend a course to improve needed skills, to read books, or talk to other people who have traveled the same path. They can tell you what to expect. In this way you will be forewarned, and to be forewarned is to be forearmed.

The point is that you have these powerful gifts of brain, energy, and time. You use these resources to manage your life or to know when and where to invest your money. All I am suggesting is that you use a little bit of these powers to save yourself from ill health. Ill health is not the automatic result of a busy life. In large measure it is the result of mindless living.

As far as money and stress are concerned, if you can afford to buy your way out of a stressful situation, don't hesitate to do it. We don't always think of our money as an antidote. The fact is that money can be a great stress reliever in more ways than one if only we would use it as such. According to Harvey MacKay, author of *How to Swim with the Sharks without Being Eaten Alive*, if you can buy your way out of a problem, you don't have a problem.

If you are taking the bus to work and you see that you are going to be late, don't just sit on the bus worried to death that you will have to face the ire of your boss or maybe lose a great client. Get off the bus at the next stop and take a taxi. You will shut down the hormonal bombardment and put yourself in a healthier state, which will empower you to be much more productive than you would be as a worried, stressed-out employee.

Remember that you can also use the love and support of the people in your life when you are about to face a stressor. Use the resource called other people as a part of your strategy to anticipate the stressor and deal with it. Don't be too shy or too proud to ask other people for help. Take a look at your calendar. Make an inventory of your crunch times and then plan active and fun times to help you cope; ask family members or colleagues to support you during those times. This will help to ward off a stress reaction.

In the same way, if you are a person of faith with any kind of spiritual connection, use your spirituality in those times of stress. Plan to go to church, spend some time in quiet meditation, or walk in nature when tough times come. If music gives you spiritual strength, stressful times are good times to listen to great music that will relax and inspire you. Plan to use your spiritual resources when you know you will be bombarded by stressful events and circumstances. Better still, keep your spiritual side strong at all times so that when stressors strike, it will be easy for you to gain inspiration from your spiritual practice.

The important point here is to give some thought beforehand to how you can use your resources (and call in some reserves) to protect yourself from potentially damaging stress effects.

Pauline was a physician with a special interest in nutrition who spent her days promoting a healthy lifestyle that would enhance heart health. Those who attended her presentations were enthusiastic about her message and many let her know later that they had been able to make some healthy changes in their lives as a result of the information she gave them.

It was a different story at home. Pauline's teenaged son Darren was becoming overweight. She knew that Darren lived for computer games and TV after school. He hated exercise with a passion but exercise was what he needed most. Her concern for his health was starting to preoccupy Pauline and she found herself losing sleep over the issue.

Pauline suggested to Darren that he join her in her daily walks so she could catch up on what was new, and spend some time with him without his siblings around. Darren suspected his mother just wanted to trick him into doing some exercise and he refused. His weight continued to creep up and Pauline was at a loss to know what to do.

It dawned on Pauline that, as a teenager, her son would love to have some extra money, and she had some she could give him. She decided to use her money as a resource to deal with her stress. She said to her son, "You're right that I want you to try some exercise. I'll give you five dollars a day if you will come for a walk with me every day for thirty straight days." Darren looked at her with deep suspicion.

Then he said, "I'll walk with you for ten bucks a day." Pauline thought that was a lot of money, but she made an agreement for thirty days for $300. By the end of thirty days her son was less resistant to the idea of exercise—he was beginning to go for a run with some of his friends after school. In a month or so he was working back to his ideal weight and his eating habits had improved because he wanted to keep up with his running pals.

Pauline's friends were shocked when she told them what Darren had negotiated. As far as Pauline was concerned, she had saved herself some sleepless nights and a whole lot of stress on her heart for $300. And she had achieved her goal. She thought $300 was a bargain.

QUICK PRESCRIPTION 13

Rx

Call Up All Your Reserves

1) Think about what you can delegate, ignore for a brief time, or hire someone else to do. You may be in the thick of a hectic time before you decide to book a cleaning service, or get someone to take over the yard work, but it can be done. Or you may want to turn that dinner with friends into a catered evening or an evening out instead of a home-cooked meal.

2) Contact those who can advise you on how to get through this stressful period—relatives, friends, or professionals.

3) Schedule some solitude to recharge your batteries—a noon visit to a sanctuary or a weekend retreat might be in order. Book a massage, or just soak in a hot bath.

4) Make sure you schedule downtime with people you enjoy and things you like to do. Rent the funniest movie you ever saw for Friday night or make sure you put on the music that makes you smile for the drive home.

QUICK STRESS QUIZ 2

Rate Your Resilience to Stress

We've dealt with the way your body responds under stress and we've talked about how to actually confront and arrest the stressor before it goes on to produce stress. Now I am going to show you how to make changes in your lifestyle as well as in your attitudes that will make you resilient in the face of trouble. The problems you encounter will not lead to a stress reaction.

Have you ever wondered why some people seem to be imperturbable and others are easily rattled? What can you do to increase your resilience in the face of a stressor? Get ready to craft your life so that you will become physiologically and mentally strong.

On a scale of 0 to 10 rate yourself with each of the following statements (10 is the highest rating you can give yourself, 0 the lowest): For example, in #8, if you can say you're the most patient person you know, give yourself a 10. If you don't know anyone with less patience, give yourself a 0.

◯—(1) I have a great love relationship and I am very happy with my partner.

◯—(2) I participate in social activities that I enjoy with others several times a month.

(3) I love my work, and look forward to going to work every day.

(4) I am never in conflict with anyone.

(5) I know I do the best I can and I don't worry or second-guess myself.

(6) I like being me. I am always happy, even when I am alone.

(7) I am an optimist. I can see a bright side to every problem.

(8) I am a patient person.

(9) I take time to relax every day.

(10) I have no financial worries.

(11) I know how to make myself happy when things go wrong.

(12) I exercise for one hour, seven days a week.

(13) I watch what I eat, avoiding excess salt, sugar, and the wrong kinds of dietary fat.

(14) I am at my ideal weight.

(15) I get at least seven hours of sleep every night.

(16) I love to help others.

(17) I have a strong faith in a higher power at work in this world.

(18) I never get angry, or if I do, I get over it very quickly.

(19) I don't hold grudges; I easily forgive people who have done things to hurt me.

(20) I find that things that cause other people stress do not have a negative effect on me.

Add up your scores. If your total is more than 100 points, you can still make improvements to protect yourself against stress. Look at the areas where you scored the lowest and work on those areas of your life. If your score is less than 100, you need to make some significant changes in your attitudes to make yourself more resilient in the face of life's stressors. Pay special attention to the areas where your score is less than 5 out of 10.

Read Part Three to find out more about stress-proofing yourself for life.

PART THREE

STRESS-PROOFING FOR LIFE

"This time, like all times, is a very good one, if we but know what to do with it."

—RALPH WALDO EMERSON, 1837

Today, more than ever, life is full of conflicting demands, sudden changes, interpersonal conflicts, and a host of little irritations. It is imperative that you build your resilience to these irritants so the negativity that is often triggered by these stressful events will not set off a stress reaction that damages your health.

You can use the **A.R.R.E.S.T.** formula when you look at upcoming, potentially stressful situations and you can:

1) **A**nticipate and plan.
2) **R**estrict the influence of the stressor.
3) **R**espond calmly, don't just react.
4) **E**stablish control over your body.
5) **S**low down and seek your inner strength.
6) **T**hink optimistically about your goals.

Beyond the immediate relief of the **A.R.R.E.S.T.** formula, you can go deeper. If you want to be really resilient in the face of stressors, you can go into training, so to speak, to raise your resistance to stressors. Use the ideas and techniques that follow to change your attitude where necessary and to improve your physical and mental fitness for a stressor-filled life.

If you use the techniques in the next two sections you will be able to transform yourself into a person with purpose, full of hope for the future, and with a deeper awareness of what is truly important to you. This perspective will help you not only change the way you respond to things that would normally distress you, but to face the events of your life with equanimity.

Hardiness in the face of stressors does not come just by making a resolution to be hardy. It involves taking the time to train yourself to become mentally and physiologically strong. This is time that you could use to make more money or to watch television, or just hang out. Instead, I am suggesting that you budget some time for your own development in order to protect yourself from stress-related health damage.

The patients I treat who have taken the time to build hardiness against stress suffer much less disease and are generally happier than those who don't think it's possible to protect themselves from the impulses that accompany stressful situations. Some people say they don't have time to practise exercises to train their autonomic nervous system to deal with stress; they neglect the human body that makes their lives possible until it breaks down. You do not need to spend a massive amount of time—just a few moments on a daily basis, used consistently, will make a big difference in your life.

How do you build hardiness against the stressors in life? The secret is to decide to take action in a few areas of your life and not to underrate their effect on your resilience. Here are the areas of concentration that we will work to develop in the next two sections:

- Make sure that you know your purpose in life. Take time to find out. As Hans Selye said, "No wind blows in favor of a ship that has no destination." Keep asking yourself the question, "Why am I here?" and live with the question on your mind. Your goal is to give yourself a clear idea of what you want to have happen in your life. Once you know what your purpose is, whenever a stressor throws an obstacle in your way, ask yourself what it is that you want to have happen. Keep your thoughts on that target. That is why an overarching purpose with goals leading in that direction is most important.

- Cultivate a deep feeling of connection with your inner spirit, with other people, and with the divine. Notice the three levels of connectedness—your inner spirit, other people, and the divine. Live your life from the promptings of your inner spirit. Live with compassion and love, reaching out to as many people as you can, and try to increase your sense of the divine.

- Choose a positive mental attitude in all situations. Find something positive in every situation and dwell on that. Tell yourself that you cannot afford even a pinch of negativity.

- Develop an acute emotional awareness. Become conscious of what your emotions are at any given moment. Practise asking yourself, "What am I feeling right now?" and acknowledging your feelings. Then use the specific techniques that follow to master your feelings and emotions, particularly when you are under pressure. That is when it really counts. Don't leave emotional control to chance.

- Develop a sense of hope for the future, especially for those times when you are feeling down. Cultivate a dauntless optimism. Adopt this motto: "Something good is going to happen to me." Say it over and over, and believe it, even in the midst of sorrow and pain. Keep looking for the good, even in the dark alleys of your life.

- Learn how to get along with others. Find ways to get along well with the really awful people in your circle. Focus on the spiritual concept that you are here to give and not to receive.

- Create physiological calm and harmony in your body by looking after yourself physically and by taking time to breathe in with awareness, letting go of tension as you exhale. Do this several times a day. Breathe and let go of tension. Do it now even as you read.

LIVING WITH PURPOSE

When I sit with patients day after day, the deeply troubling issues for them are not so much what is happening to them on the outside, but what is happening on the inside and how they really feel about their lives. For years, it's been suggested that the major causes of stress are too much to do, too little to do, lack of feedback from peers or the boss, or interpersonal conflicts. The infidelity of a spouse, or the loss of a job, or sudden, unwanted lifestyle changes are all troubling. I find, however, that if I help my patients dig to find the real cause of their discomfort, it is usually related to the way they feel about their lives, and their level of positive regard for themselves.

Build resilience to stressors by developing your understanding of why you are here in the world at this time, and embrace one or two basic things that you want to do with your life. Try not to go to bed tonight without first affirming and believing that you are here for a reason. Accept the fact that your appearance on the planet is no accident—assume that you are here to accomplish some special mission. Think of yourself as an emissary, sent here to do something wonderful in the world. It does not need to be a mission to save the world all by yourself. If you commit yourself to act with love, compassion, and discipline within your own sphere—within your family, your circle of friends, your workplace, or your community—with the good of the world in mind, that will be enough. But the determination to find a way to add value to the world by living purposefully in it must be ingrained in your soul.

If, like many of us, you do not yet know what your purpose is, ask yourself the question every day and eventually the answer will appear. Gather ideas by talking to other people who seem inspired by life, learning more about the things that stir your imagination, and listening to your heart in silent contemplation. Look back over your experiences for the things that gave you the most satisfaction, and try to discover why. Assess your strengths and your special talents. Make a list of them and decide how you want to use them. Talk to family and friends. Maybe they will remind you of the things you were passionate about when you were younger. Don't dismiss those youthful dreams.

Spend a little time every day getting to know yourself, your values, and your aspirations. Take the time to write down and think about the things you value most in life, and listen to the promptings of your soul. Learn to live from a greater depth of spirit, as Emerson says.

What kind of person do you want to be? What is it that you want to accomplish with your life? Where do you want to have an impact?

Once you discover your purpose, make it the foundation of all that you do. You will become more confident of your value in the world and in your community if you have a firm purpose in life. Your purpose will set the stage for positive feelings to flow through your body and mind and these feelings will add energy to your actions.

As you define your purpose, visualize it. Articulate it from your heart. Choose one or two great thoughts that sum it up. Be daring—don't rely on mediocre thoughts. Fortune favors the bold, so make those thoughts inspirational. Write them down and keep them posted in a prominent place so you will be reminded of them frequently. This is how you become a person "on purpose." Committing yourself to fulfillment of your purpose and living your life in alignment with that purpose is a marvelous defense against stress. It will increase your sense of self-worth. Your purpose will push you in the direction you want to go, and positive emotions will surround you.

Your plans and goals should help you accomplish your purpose. You should be able to define a vision and related goals that govern your career, your health, your finances, your spiritual development, and how you relate to your family. Make your goals specific, inspiring, personal, attainable, and measurable. Make the outcomes vivid in your mind. Practise seeing yourself as having achieved each of your goals and make sure that each goal is in keeping with your overall purpose. Then take action to achieve your goals.

Living with purpose is a lifelong project and requires persistence on your part. There are tough times ahead and your purpose should always be clear. Keep your great thoughts in mind during times of stress and tension. Choose to think wonderful, positive thoughts when obstacles are surrounding you.

As you achieve your goals, stay open and leave room for change as you proceed. Beware of rigidity and be prepared to revisit your purpose and fine-tune it as your experience grows—to live is to change.

After years in the classroom, Barry was appointed assistant dean at his college. Friends and family congratulated him on his success and teased him about his fancy new office and his sudden acquisition of support staff. Many of them were surprised when he resigned a couple of years later, and took a job teaching at a smaller school. For Barry, it wasn't a difficult decision.

"As assistant dean, I spent all my time in meetings, staring at reports, sweating over budgets, or mediating disputes. I made more money than I'm making now, but I was miserable. I couldn't figure out why, because this is the career track for academics and I was lucky to get the opportunity. But then I remembered why I had gone into teaching in the first place. As I talked to some of the people that I went to school with—it's amazing who comes out of the woodwork when you become a big 'success'—I remembered being fired up about teaching and about connecting with students and ideas. I realized that while I was assistant dean, I wasn't ever going to experience the thrill that comes from making those connections again. I talked it over with my wife, and the more we talked together and to the kids, the more we realized that what was best for me—and the most important example I could set for our kids—was to walk the talk. If teaching was what mattered to me, then teaching was what I should be doing. My kids know that their lifestyle is going to be affected by this change, but they also know they have a dad who is true to his purpose. Just their luck they didn't get a dad who thought his purpose was to be really rich . . ."

QUICK PRESCRIPTION 14

Define Your Purpose

1) Spend five minutes every day alone and think about what your purpose in life is. Just think about yourself and what you are meant to do in this world. Work on developing a deep sense of purpose; let it capture your full attention for five minutes every day. This alone is bound to enrich your life.

2) At the end of your five minutes, summarize, in one sentence, your answer to the question, "What is the purpose of my life?"

3) Work on refining your description of your purpose and what it means as you live your life every day.

CHOOSING YOUR COMMITMENTS

Once you have begun to define your purpose in life, your next step is to align your actions with it. Are you doing things that will help you achieve your purpose?

If you are putting energy into activities that are not in harmony with your purpose, you will feel stressed as a result of the conflict. Once you've settled on your purpose in life, commit yourself to it. Let every action be guided by the purpose you want to fulfill. Living consciously and deliberately means that your commitments are aligned with your purpose.

Studies have demonstrated over and over that commitment to a purpose is one of the best buffers against stress both at home and at work. If you find your life's purpose, and remain uncommitted to it, your life will soon be full of inconsistencies. It is these inconsistencies that cause the kind of mental confusion and anguish that breeds stress. You know that if you waffle on your commitment to your spouse, your marriage will soon be full of stress. If you waffle on your commitment to your job, your work life will soon be full of stress. If you waffle on your commitment to your purpose, your life will soon be full of stress.

If your day-to-day actions aren't aligned with your purpose—and the values and principles that go along with it—it will be difficult to think well of yourself and to avoid the stress that comes from internal turmoil. Honoring your commitment to your purpose and your values will bring wholeness and integrity to your life.

Look at every area of your life and count your commitments. Can you live up to all those commitments? Are they all in harmony with each other and your life's purpose? If a particular commitment is not in harmony with your purpose, eliminate or replace it. Don't allow neighbors, friends, or family to hold you to a commitment that does not ring true to you.

If you are in a committed relationship, take a good look at it. Do you really want this relationship? Is it important to you, or are you there because you think anything is better than nothing? Once you decide that you really want your relationship, take action to enrich and enjoy it. Spend at least 20 minutes every day honoring your commitment to the most important person in your life. Don't say you are committed to someone and do nothing about it. Never take your lover for granted. Not even for a day. If you ignore your relationship with your partner, you are headed for stress—and you will likely be a stressor in your partner's life as well.

If you are a parent, are you committed to being a great parent? Do you consciously honor your commitment no matter what is happening? Do your kids get first crack at your time and energy or do you prefer TV, newspapers, tennis, or golf? If you are committed to your kids, let your commitment to them reign. Let it govern the way you live your life.

Take a look at your work. Are you committed to doing a wonderful job? Commit yourself to putting a stamp of excellence on your job whether it's an interim position or a long-term one. If you have the job only for six months, be committed to it for six months. No hesitation. No ambiguity. Either do the job well or leave and find something you can fully commit yourself to.

Greg is a Seattle real estate agent with a large clientele and a good reputation. Word of his success led to a call from a Hong Kong multimillionaire. To Greg's great delight, the rich man hired Greg to help him buy a property in the area.

The customer flew in to meet with Greg and take a last look at the property before they finalized the deal. It was worth several million dollars. All was well. Then the client asked if Greg could get the paperwork done and close the deal before he left for Hong Kong. Greg hesitated and said, "The paperwork won't be done until late in the afternoon. I'm sorry, but I can't meet you then to do the review because that's when I play basketball with my son."

The customer was so impressed by Greg's commitment to his family that instead of turning away, he changed his flight. He wanted this kind of man to represent him. And Greg's behavior was contagious. It had a positive effect on the way the customer treated his own family.

QUICK PRESCRIPTION 15

Rx

Align Your Commitments

1) Review what you've written as you've defined your purpose in life.
2) Make a list of all your commitments: at home, at work, and in your community.
3) Review your commitments and mark them according to whether they are in harmony with your purpose or if you have moved beyond them.
4) Weed out those commitments that are not aligned with your purpose.
5) Rededicate yourself to the commitments that are central to your purpose in life.

AFFIRMING YOUR BELIEFS

Your beliefs have enormous power. They really can influence the way you feel. As you think about your life and your purpose, ask yourself what positive things you believe about yourself, your environment, and life itself.

You may find that the room in your head where you keep your beliefs is full of negative beliefs. Many of us never progress beyond the beliefs we adopted as children or our beliefs tell us only what we can't do or what is wrong with us or the world around us. If this is your situation, I would like you to go into that room and remove all the imposters—the negative beliefs that are taking up space in your head. Eliminate your negative beliefs and concentrate on the positive beliefs that you have, especially about yourself. Your beliefs are your own choice so you might as well choose to believe things that will uplift your life.

You may find that the room where you keep your beliefs is empty—devoid of the magical element that can be so crucial to your success in life. If you have no beliefs at all, you should begin to fill the room with positive beliefs that will help you achieve your purpose in life and help you make sense of the world.

Carry positive beliefs with you wherever you go. Don't leave home without that bundle of positive beliefs that make you feel good about yourself, about other people, and about life. Refuse to entertain beliefs that do not give you power or support you. Whenever I go to my office or give a speech to an audience, I always carry a bellyful of positive beliefs with me. I say to myself, "I believe that I will be very helpful to my patients today," or "I believe that the members of the association I am addressing are going to be greatly helped by what I have to say."

In addition to this type of custom-made belief, try to cultivate and affirm a strong belief in your own significance as a human being in the wider context of your family, your community, and the world. This is where your purpose and your commitment to it will give you strength.

Don't just believe in a casual manner, ignoring your basic philosophy and faith until times get tough. Devote awareness, thought, and passion to the things that you believe in. Enliven them with the fire of your attention. Put them into practice. This will go a long way to help you control the kinds of emotions that flow through your nervous system when a stressor appears.

Craig and Alison dedicated their lives to celebrating nature and the outdoors. Craig worked in conservation and encouraged their children, when they were very young, to get out and enjoy natural beauty and the challenges that came with it. All three of their sons grew up with a healthy respect and enthusiasm for nature, and all of them stayed active in the outdoors—climbing, skiing, canoeing, and trekking—after they graduated from university and as they began their own careers in biology, geology, and forestry.

The close-knit clan was devastated when Ian, the youngest son, was killed in a vacation mountaineering accident. In the days after the funeral Craig and Alison and their older sons found it hard to keep going on.

Friends remained attentive to the family members, who relied on their inner strength for consolation.

As Craig put it, "I've always believed that the boys should do what they loved and I always encouraged them to do so. Holding them back was never an option. They all believe in taking risks and being out there in the natural world. This is a terrible, terrible loss for us, but we have to respect Ian's choices and his life, which was so rich and which made him feel so fulfilled. His life was too short, but he got such joy out of it. He told me that the mountains were where he felt closest to God, and we'll just have to surrender him to that. We're going to have to content ourselves with being thankful for the time that we had Ian with us. It's not going to be easy."

QUICK PRESCRIPTION 16

Rx

Experience the Magic of Belief

1) Write down as many of your beliefs as you can think of.

2) Look over the list and choose five positive beliefs that can empower you to serve your purpose in life, for example, "I believe that I can make a positive difference in the world around me."

3) Concentrate on these five beliefs and give them a place in your heart and your life.

BUILDING A POSITIVE MENTAL AND EMOTIONAL STATE

EMOTIONS ARE IMPULSES of energy that accompany every action, thought, and experience. You are never without emotions, but if you're like most of us, you tend to ignore them unless they erupt too violently or loom too large. They are forever around, vying for your attention and yet it is hard to define what they really are.

Each of your emotions has an attendant chemical state. The emotions of fear or love, for example, will have their own chemistry, while the emotions of anger, sadness, or joy will each have a different chemistry. We assume that the emotion generates the chemistry, but with practice, you can reverse the process. You can trigger the underlying chemistry and experience the emotion of your choice by acting and thinking in a manner that is consistent with the emotion that you want to feel. Act sad and you will feel sad, for example. Better still, act happy and you will feel happy.

We all know that you cannot heal some emotional states as readily as you can heal an injured finger. Although we cannot change emotions instantly, we can still make the change. We can create the emotions that we want to feel. Isn't it wonderful to know that we have such awesome power?

In Quick Prescription 2, you began to practise emotional awareness. This is the first step in learning to change your emotions. Now that you're more aware of your emotions, how can you change them?

When a stressor appears in your life, if you perceive it as something that is threatening and beyond your control, the limbic system in your brain will produce a bundle of energy called a negative emotion. This will happen as an immediate reaction to the stressful experience you are facing and change your emotional state. Negative emotions such as fear, anger, worry, guilt, or resentment are like unexpected visitors to your home; they're probably okay for a short while, but if they stay too long, they wear out the furniture and disrupt the normal routine of the household, so to speak. Overall, they have a negative effect on your psycho-physiological system.

You want to be able to change your houseguests. Do this by using your emotional awareness to flag any negative emotion that tries to take up residence. Make your mind an emotion filter, letting only the positive ones through. This is what a cell membrane does. Cell membranes are very selective. They stop the passage of dangerous substances and let in only the nutritious compounds that support life. Your mind must do the same thing. When negative emotions appear, don't let them pass and contaminate your sacred inner terrain.

When the emotions of anger, sadness, resentment, guilt, or fear appear, recognize them. Keep them around long enough to learn from them. But you must stay in control. Depending on the situation, you may even choose to stay with that emotion for a given time. It should always be for a defined time and not be allowed to drag on.

If you didn't get a promotion you were expecting, you may decide that you are going to be angry about it for a day. That is okay. You will likely learn something as long as you don't allow yourself to be overwhelmed by your anger. Just remember to stay in control and see what you can get out of the experience.

Control is the key to a healthy immune response, according to many studies.

When the anger no longer serves a useful purpose, move on. Decide to create the emotions you want to feel instead. Set about doing what you need to do in order to fill your mind with the positive emotions that you want to feel. Instead of anger and resentment, maybe you can choose hope for success of the organization and yourself. Be hopeful even when you are struggling with the idea that you could have been in that corner office or doing a better job of chairing the meeting. Fill your head with positive, self-enhancing emotions and you will also be filling your body with the corresponding chemicals that strengthen and support your life.

There is nothing illegal or unhealthy about knowing how to turn angry moments into hopeful ones, or hateful feelings into loving ones. It is easy to feel angry, unhappy, hateful, or guilty. It is easy to go along with the suffering. What is hard is to suspend your first reaction, and understand an emotion as it presents itself. It is not easy to exert the discipline to change that negative emotion into a positive one, especially when you are under pressure. But if you do, it will make your life more fulfilling, despite the stressors.

Joe and his brother, Nick, get together for lunch once a month. After they'd ordered, Nick said, "So, how did the weekend with the mother-in-law go?"

"She seems to have finally resigned herself to the fact that I'm married to her daughter," Joe replied. "Now she's decided to change me into the kind of person she thinks Val should have picked. This time, it was my clothes she didn't like. Sara's husband doesn't wear running shoes all the

time. Her son Rob doesn't wear jeans and flannel shirts. Fortunately, the first time she started on me, I had my mouth full and by the time I could reply, my brain had kicked in to steer me away from a snarky comeback. I caught myself getting angry and switched gears. I just nodded.

"Then I followed up by asking her if she needed any work done around the place. I was determined to treat her the same way I would if I liked her—I wasn't going to spend two days angry and upset. I wanted good feelings, so I acted and spoke as though I was feeling good. By the end of the weekend, her garden, basement, and garage were tidied up; mother-in-law was forced to be gracious and thank me; and *I scored major brownie points with Val." Joe smiled. "So the weekend wasn't too bad."*

QUICK PRESCRIPTION 17

Rx

Use Your Emotional Awareness (Emotional Redirection Part 1)

1) As soon as a stressor crops up, notice the emotions that are prompted and that affect your body. Ask yourself, "What exactly am I feeling: fear, frustration, a desire for revenge? What?" Name the emotion.

2) When you detect a negative emotion, stop for a moment. Notice that you are being pulled into the loser's corner. Recall that harboring anger, fear, guilt, hatred, or sadness will compromise your health.

3) Decide to choose a positive emotion to replace the negative one.

CHANGING YOUR NEGATIVE EMOTIONS

You cannot live without experiencing negative emotions like fear, hostility, resentment, frustration, and sadness. You are only human. You are built to generate both positive and negative emotions, and it's easy to hang on to negative ones. You must, however, recognize and master them. You can fill your head with positive emotions and crowd out the negative ones. Be so full of life-enhancing feelings that they overflow into your words, attitudes, and actions, leaving no room for negative emotions.

Emotions are somewhere between your thoughts and your actions, and the more you think a particular thought or act out a particular emotion, the more your feelings will change. Use your thoughts, your self-talk, and your actions to help you change your current negative feelings to the feelings that you want to experience. What you tell yourself does affect the kinds of emotions (and chemicals) that flow through your system. If you are always muttering in dissatisfaction, telling yourself how terrible things are and how unhappy you feel, you are programming yourself to experience negative feelings. If you take control of your internal monologue; ditch the negative, self-defeating talk; and begin to tell yourself positive things, you will improve your ability to perform even in the most stressful situation.

Choose to cultivate positive emotions by concentrating on images and feelings that uplift you.

Filter out an undesirable emotion by thinking of the positive opposite—the emotion you want to experience. Begin to act the way you want to feel. Laugh and smile if you want to feel happy. Walk with confidence and keep your eyes focused on the person you are addressing if you want to look and feel confident. See the other person's point of view and express it if you want to be understanding. Let go of vengeful thoughts and ill feelings against anyone who has hurt you and aim to do something good for them if you want to experience the incredible lightness of forgiveness, and so on.

Visualize yourself being full of the emotion that you want. Ask yourself, "How would I like to feel? How would I like to be perceived? What emotions would I like to emulate?" Then put in your mind an image of yourself with those emotions. Your mind thinks in pictures. If you want to feel love instead of hatred, think of someone you love. Create an image of yourself and that person together and let the emotion sink in so that it can change your behavior. See yourself feeling and expressing love. Imagine whatever emotion you want to feel. Imagine in earnest and the emotion will materialize. The more frequently you practise this imagery technique, the more easily and quickly the desired emotions will surface when you summon them.

If it is joy that you want to feel, assume the posture and the behavior that you would have if you were feeling joyful. Or ask yourself, "If I were enthusiastic about this situation, what would I be thinking? What images would be in my mind? What feelings would I have? How would I be carrying myself? How would I act?" And begin to think and act in a way that is consistent with the emotion you want to experience. The bottom line here is to know how you want to feel and then make the effort to make those feelings a physiological reality. Acting out the desired emotion and bringing your thoughts in line with it is just one way to do it.

Another way to help yourself redirect your emotions is to gather visual aids to help you trigger positive emotions—perhaps pictures of your family, a happy time with friends, or a favorite pet; or post a great poem or an award you received. Put them in your office or at home where you will see them when you need to remind yourself of a more positive feeling.

Earlier, you did a Quick Checkup and found a memory of when you felt really good. Use that memory now, or recall memories of situations when you experienced specific emotions that you would like to experience more often. Practise recalling those memories and embellish them in your mind. Choose a memory of a time when you were energetic, one when you were joyful, and one when you were particularly relaxed, calm, and confident. Search your experience for three such situations and expand on them, remembering and highlighting the emotional part of the experience. Think of these three situations often and experience the corresponding feelings that went along with them. Every time you are threatened by a negative emotion, open your chest of memories and choose one of these positive situations and focus on it until the accompanying emotions pour into your body and mind.

Music can also go a long way in helping you to change your emotions. Music influences physiology because the sound waves affect cells and their functioning. Choose pieces of music that create the specific emotions you want to generate. Make a tape or a CD with three different types of music that represent three types of positive emotions. I recommend that you create your own CD or tape of music to stimulate happy feelings when you are sad. Also find some music to help you to feel relaxed, calm, and confident and other pieces to generate feelings of energy and inspiration.

As an additional strategy for changing your emotions, spend time in pleasant situations and go out of your way to find individuals who radiate the kinds of emotions you want to feel. Be around people who are happy if you want to generate happiness. Ask yourself where you are likely to discover the feelings that you want and take yourself there. In other words, take some control over the emotional content of your surroundings.

Bev and Jenn came out of their client meeting feeling shell-shocked. They knew that the client's wife was gravely ill, and they knew that there had been some problems with product quality during the last quarter. They had thought, however, that their team had acted promptly to solve the quality problems, which were not serious. Nothing had prepared them for the blast they got. When they came out of the meeting they felt as if they'd been attacked personally as well as professionally. They got into Bev's car and sat there.

"Well," Bev said. "That was something. I've been in this business for thirty years, and I don't think I've ever been taken down quite so thoroughly. I feel terrible."

Jenn said, "I've only been in it for two years, but I don't think I want to stay if this is what it's like. How do you stand it?"

"If I was alone in the car, I'd get out my 'cranky client' music and sing."

"What?!"

Bev said, "A long time ago, I decided that whenever I had a really bad time with a client, I wasn't going to let it ruin the way I was feeling. I wasn't going to let it become personal. I made a tape—which my son has turned into a CD—to get me out of my post-meeting funk, and help me feel better. It's in the glove compartment. It's going to show my age big time, but I think we need it. Get it out and put it in the player, kid."

The Rolling Stones opened with "You Can't Always Get What You Want." Jenn scoffed. By the time "Satisfaction" came on, she was smiling and humming along. Bev, Jenn, and the Beatles did "Obla-di, Obla-da" (Jenn was on the air tambourine), and they rolled into their office parking lot singing "All You Need Is Love." They got some strange looks as they were driving back to the office, but when a coworker asked Bev how the meeting had gone, she was able to smile and shrug, "Not the most fun I ever had, but it's over."

QUICK PRESCRIPTION 18

Rx

Shift Emotional Gears
(Emotional Redirection Part 2)

1) Practise some of the techniques for emotional redirection that have been outlined: spend time reinforcing some of your great memories, gather your visual aids, choose your music, and learn about how you feel and act when you're enjoying a positive emotional state.

2) As soon as you notice a stressor is causing emotional upset, say to yourself over and over again, "This too will pass and until it does, I refuse to let it compromise my health." Practise saying it right now: "This too will pass and until it does, I refuse to let it compromise my health."

3) Choose the emotion that is the opposite of the one that is suddenly disturbing you by calling up your memories, playing music, or using whatever techniques you have practised to inspire the feeling you want to experience.

THE BEST EMOTIONS TO CHOOSE

There is a long list of positive emotions you can choose to replace the negative ones that may be trying to take over your mind (and body) in stressful times. Key ones are gratitude, hope, enthusiasm, confidence, compassion, tolerance, love, joy, and inner peace and harmony. I want you to think about these in a new and personal way. Try to experience the emotions as often as possible. Live with them in mind. Despite the fact that you are busy with your life, you need to take the time to reflect on and remember these emotions so that you can experience and summon them when you need them. If you fill your mind with these emotions, the challenges of your life will sparkle with opportunities. The difficulties you face will be catalysts to help you succeed in the face of all that comes and goes. Your stress level will plummet with these positive emotions on board, even though the stress level of others under similar conditions may be spiraling off the chart.

Let me repeat the emotions again and I am going to ask you to experience them in a new way as you read: gratitude, hope, enthusiasm, confidence, compassion, tolerance, love, joy, and inner peace and harmony. Make these emotions an important part of your life. Pay attention to how they feel to you; practise feeling them. Behave with them in mind and you will be a big winner in life. Remember that the primary stressor in your life is any negative emotion that you entertain. If instead you fill your soul with the emotions we have highlighted, stress will not be a problem. Let me ask you this: How can you be stressed when you are full of gratitude, hopeful about the future, enthusiastic about your life, confident, compassionate, tolerant of others, loving, joyful, and relaxed inside and out?

Here is a quick overview:

- Gratitude is a decision. When you find yourself in a stressful situation, choose to be grateful for something. Focus on what is good about your life. Take nothing for granted. Make an effort to feel and express appreciation for everything around you. Say thanks wherever and whenever it is appropriate. If you become obsessed with being grateful, you will notice the good things about your life and this will help you to feel and function better. Practise being grateful when things are going well and you will find it easier to be thankful during times of stress.

- Think hopeful thoughts in the face of a stressor. It does not matter how pessimistic you tend to be—the message of this book is that you can change. You can transform yourself into an optimistic person. Hope is the deliberate act of expecting that good things will happen to you. Internalize the belief that something positive will come from the predicament you are facing. Say over and over again to yourself, "Something good is going to come out of this." Say it with conviction and believe it in your heart until it becomes a permanent part of your thinking. Look for the positive aspects as things unfold.

- To live with enthusiasm means that you are living your life with delight from a deeper sense of being. You are capable of greatness. Gladstone, a former prime minister of England, once said that all of us are born to be great and are capable of doing some great work in the world. Emerson, the American philosopher, said that nothing great has ever been done without enthusiasm. So decide to adopt this emotion and live your life with gusto.

- Confidence comes from peeling away the doubts and fears you have adopted and getting down to your pristine, authentic self—the one you have affirmed in your beliefs about yourself, your talents, and your skills.

- Decide now that you will act with compassion. Begin to care. Care is a verb—an action word. Initiate your program of compassion today by practicing "random acts of kindness." Do it and see how it feels.

- The tolerance that comes with compassion can protect you from stress. The number one cause of stress in my patients is other people. Money or work-related stressors are far behind. To be tolerant you must remind yourself that we are different from each other; our ambitions, our beliefs, and our interests will clash, and the resulting stress can invade your sacred territory. When you adopt compassion and tolerance as constant companions in your life, you want good things for yourself and for others, and you will hold a deep respect for others. This means being able to accept another's point of view. When you live like this, you feel good about yourself and you will start to bring out the goodwill in those around you.

- When you are full of love, you suffer less stress because when you love you tend to be more relaxed. Choose to love everyone, even if you hate what they do, or what they represent. Learn to separate the acts from the people, and give the people your love. If you don't know how to love those who constantly rub you the wrong way, act as if you love them. Begin to behave in those ways and slowly the feelings of love will begin to flow. Love will banish many negative emotions from your mind, lessening the stress and increasing your enjoyment of life. The moment you choose love, magical things begin to happen. Act in love, give your love to those around you through acts of kindness and the stress (not the stressors) will be extinguished. Love and the resulting peace and joy will keep you calm in the midst of all that comes and goes.

- To generate joy, think about a joyful event or situation, imagine a happy outcome or a happy scene, assume the attitude of a joyful person. Walk, talk, and carry yourself as if you are happy to produce feelings of joy.

- You cannot have inner peace and be stressed at the same time. In a practical sense, we all know what inner peace feels like. We have all had at least short bursts of it. The real question is how do you generate inner peace when all around you is falling apart? When your boss is frowning at you, you have just lost a big sale, your spouse is putting you down, or your friends seem to have forsaken you, how do you let go of the tension and turn your inner turmoil into peace? Practise the "soft eyes" technique outlined in Quick Prescription 11 to slow down and go to your inner strength. That is where you will find power. That is where you will find the divine. Be still on a regular basis and generate inner peace and calm.

By taking control of your emotional state, and filling your mind with positive emotions of gratitude, hope, enthusiasm, confidence, compassion, tolerance, love, joy, and inner peace and harmony, you will put yourself far away from the arena of stress.

Marg had always programmed gratitude into her life. If something didn't work out, she chose to be grateful for what she had. If her flight was late, she chose to be grateful that she'd arrived safely and that she'd had the chance to travel. The stress that could have been caused by disappointments was always negated by her decision to be grateful.

As she aged, the disappointments became greater. One of the biggest blows came when she was diagnosed with macular degeneration. That, plus glaucoma, robbed her of her sight at a time when her body was becoming frail. Her active lifestyle became more and more restricted. She even had to leave the choir she loved to sing in. Instead of becoming bitter at the challenges of old age, she was genuinely grateful for the opportunities she had had during her life. As she explained, "Some people never had the experiences I've been able to enjoy. I got to sing in the choir for years. My son has set the stations on my receiver so I can tune in and hear choirs from around the world. People I used to sing with still get in touch with me. I've been very lucky."

Despite her problems, Marg's general health remained good and she was still able to enjoy life.

QUICK PRESCRIPTION 19

Make an Emotional Choice (Emotional Redirection Part 3)

1) When negative emotions are overwhelming you, changing your emotions can seem like an impossible task. Gratitude is one of the easiest places to begin your journey back to a positive emotional state. Visit gratitude daily to make sure you can always take that first step. Every morning before you get out of bed, think of three things that you are thankful for. Hold yourself back on the edge of the bed if you must and reflect—"Three things that I can be thankful for." By cultivating an attitude of gratitude, you are setting yourself up to feel good during the day.

2) In times of a negative emotional storm, again move yourself to gratitude and remind yourself of your good fortune. Then relax your body by doing one of the breathing and relaxation exercises you've practised. Hasten the departure of disturbing negative emotions and deepen your inner peace by letting go and allowing your mind to become still as you breathe and focus on your breath. Keep breathing deeply and allow every thought that approaches to pass through and out of your mind while you just continue to breathe in and out and experience the quieting response to this exercise.

3) Use your preferred techniques to move your emotional state to a better place. Choose from hope, enthusiasm, confidence, compassion, tolerance, love, joy, or inner peace and harmony. They are all there for the taking.

BUILDING PHYSIOLOGICAL HARMONY

An optimal level of physical fitness and performance is one of the most important components of your armor against stress. (Notice that I did not say "an Olympic level.") Your stress response is mostly physical, and stress damages your body. The functions of your brain, glands, liver, pancreas, and heart change when you give in to a stress reaction. The more you can improve your physical resilience, the stronger you will be and the more physical control you will have when stressors come your way. You also reap the benefits of a more relaxed, healthier life when you become more physically fit and improve your body's performance.

Physical fitness is the ability to move and work without getting tired. People who are physically fit tend to do better work and still suffer less stress. When you are not fit, your body will tire easily and you will likely feel sluggish both in mind and body, compared to how much more alive you could really feel.

Other factors that affect your physical performance can also be adjusted and improved. Here I'm thinking about the way you breathe, the way you stand and sit, how much sleep you get, and what you choose to eat and drink every day. Breathing deeply, evenly, and consciously; assuming a more balanced posture; and making sure that the right side of your body and the left are equally relaxed are not difficult habits to adopt and they will significantly improve the way you feel and the way you cope every day. Also, do not ignore the obvious. Pay attention to your sleep pattern and your nutrition. Know what is right for you. Get some help from your doctor or a dietitian if you need to, and change your lifestyle as necessary. Your goal is physiological harmony, and a deep sense of stillness and confidence is one of the gifts available to a person who achieves it.

Use the sections that follow to assess your physical condition as well as your daily habits. A well-conditioned body will suffer less tension and you will have a calmer mind. As a bonus, a high level of physical fitness will transform the cells of your body into economical users of energy and your energy reserves will increase.

Jim had been tired all the time lately—too tired to muster much enthusiasm for work, or for play, for that matter. He was stressed out from all the demands on him and his inability to meet them. The slightest challenge seemed to knock him flat and he decided it had something to do with the fact that he was aging. He felt so lousy that he finally decided to get some medical attention.

When he got in to see his doctor, he said, "I think there's something wrong with me. I'm tired all the time. Just a regular day's activity wears me out. I need some medication to pep me up and get me going. Maybe there are some tests that you could do to find out what's wrong with me."

His doctor smiled and said, "Okay, we'll look into all the angles. First, tell me about your lifestyle. . . ."

QUICK CHECKUP

What Kind of Shape Are You in?

1) Are you tired at the end of your regular workday? (Are you tired by the time you're ready to go to work?)
2) When you choose what to eat, do you pick food that gives you lasting energy and nourishes you or food that distracts and pleases you?
3) During the last seven nights, what time did you go to bed, how long did you sleep without waking, what time did you get up?

BREATHE, FOR GOODNESS' SAKE, BREATHE

Although you've been breathing since the second you were born, I want you to turn your attention to this act that we all take for granted. Earlier when we talked about sidestepping a stress reaction, we talked about breathing with awareness. In many of the prescriptions we begin to take control of our reaction by taking a deep breath. When you confront a stressful situation, your breathing tends to become shallow. It is crucial to your health that you remember to practise slow, deep, even, conscious breathing whenever you have to speak up at a meeting, meet an irritating client, or deal with an angry child or coworker.

Make a point of focusing your awareness on your breathing. With practice, you can induce a sense of physiological harmony by breathing with full awareness before you rush into action. This will help you change your response to the stressors in your life to one of calm and reason. Refuse to be like a wound-up toy waiting to be triggered into action. Breathe to remain calm and steady in the midst of all that comes and goes. Those mundane little stressors just won't have the same power to knock you off your stride.

Breathing with awareness is the first step in improving the way you breathe. As long as you breathe with mindful awareness, you are improving your odds against the unhealthy effects of a stress response. Breathe deeply and completely whenever you get a chance.

Many of my patients who practise conscious, deep breathing have found that if they do it in response to stressful situations for a while, eventually it becomes an automatic response. This means that your brain will remember to tell your body to breathe deeply when you are faced with a stressor. As you practise breathing with full awareness, you may begin to notice that you are automatically breathing more deeply all the time, with a resulting increase in physiological harmony and calm. There is a whole world of amazing benefits waiting for you on the other side of a deep breath.

Beyond breathing with awareness is a technique called abdominal breathing. Once you have mastered the art of breathing deeply and consciously, you can begin to adopt abdominal breathing and make it a habit. This type of breathing is superior to the way we usually breathe. We all remember being told, "Chest out! Stomach in!" With abdominal breathing, your stomach rises as you breathe in and falls as you breathe out. I advise patients who come to see me about stress to first just breathe with awareness, and then to learn and practise abdominal breathing until it becomes routine.

Like breath awareness, you can practise abdominal breathing at any time. But you must get a feel for it before you start practising it at random.

Take a series of deep, relaxing breaths several times during the day. Make your abdomen rise as you breathe in and fall as you breathe out; let your muscles relax, even become loose and limp. Focus on your center, two inches below your navel and breathe slowly in (feeling your belly rise) and out (feeling your belly fall) as you become more and more relaxed.

As you breathe in, observe your body and move your awareness from your toes up to your head. As you breathe out, smile and feel a wave of relaxation moving down from your head through your face, down through your neck, arms, chest, abdomen, legs, and feet. This is a simple but very powerful practice. Do it right now. Breathe in, bringing your mind all the way up from your toes to your head; breathe out, feeling a wave of deep relaxation moving slowly down into your arms and legs. Don't forget to smile, and when you do, smile with your whole body. Send the message of your smile echoing throughout every cell in your body. How can you be stressed when you live like this?

Use any little irritation—an unfriendly look, a jam in the photocopier, a computer freeze, a coffee spill—as a cue to take a series of relaxing breaths. Smile with your whole body, breathe in and let all your muscles become heavy and warm. Do it with the intention of inducing calm deep inside you.

Shelley had to present a report at a monthly departmental meeting. The last time she did a presentation she was a wreck and she was becoming more agitated about the meeting as the day got closer.

"I'll probably pass out. I felt so light-headed last time."

"I wouldn't be surprised if you did pass out this time," said her co-worker. "You're in a sweat and practically hyperventilating just thinking about your presentation now. If you do that in the meeting, there's no way you'll get enough air when you're speaking."

"I always do that when I get nervous. You should have seen me at my wedding. My voice was so faint, the minister couldn't even hear me. How will I relax and get through it? I'm not getting any better at this!"

"Well, forget all that stuff about picturing the audience in their underwear—yuck, don't even go there. Concentrate on your breathing. That's where confidence comes from—you've got to connect with what's inside as you breathe. Take some time to breathe in and out during your presentation—a little silence won't kill any of your audience. In fact, it will be less stressful for the rest of us. The last time we were so worried that you wouldn't get through your bit without collapsing that I don't think we heard a word you said."

QUICK PRESCRIPTION 20

Master the Art of Abdominal Breathing

1) Choose a time when you have a few minutes. Lie on your back or sit in a comfortable, upright position.

2) Put one hand, palm down, on your abdomen, two inches below your navel.

3) As you breathe in, make sure your abdomen pushes your hand out, and as you breathe out, your abdomen (and your hand) should sink.

4) Say to yourself, "Breathing in, I observe my body and mind," and, "Breathing out, I smile and relax."

5) Once you've practised, try abdominal breathing without using your hand. You can practise abdominal breathing at any time, even if you are talking to a prospective buyer, attending a meeting, or sitting watching television.

STAND UP FOR YOURSELF

As you work to improve your breathing, you may notice that you are struggling to take a deep breath. If you are like many of us, this may have a lot to do with the way you stand and sit. If you are slouched, with your shoulders slumped forward, you will not be able to open your chest enough to get a good supply of air into your lungs. This posture can also affect circulation to vital organs in your body.

In addition, your "hot spots" where you habitually hold muscle tension—whether you're under the influence of a stressor or not—are probably pulling your body out of alignment. This will also affect your posture and your breathing. Poor posture not only makes it hard for you to breathe properly, it also affects the way you walk and sit, and makes it harder for you to relax your muscles.

You need to at least check your posture, but most likely you need to take some simple steps to correct it. When you are going through stressful times, check your posture regularly. Notice how you are sitting or standing. See if you are straining any particular muscles and correct your posture by trying to induce a sense of balance in your body. Be aware of pressure situations when you are likely to slouch or contract your muscles unnecessarily and throw your body out of kilter.

Follow these steps to check (or correct) your body's alignment. *Please note: If there's something wrong with your back, neck, or pelvis, you should get specific advice from a physician. This book is not intended to treat a condition, but to help you deal with the effects of stress.*

- Begin with your head and neck: Bend your head forward until your chin is almost touching your chest or until you can feel tension at the back of your neck. Of course, your head is too far forward; bring it back until you feel tension in the front of your neck. This tells you that your head is too far back. Now move your head to a position between these two points where there is no tension. That is where your head should be—high and not too far forward or back.

- Next, check your lateral alignment to see if your head is too much to the left or to the right. Turn your head to the left until you feel tension in the right side of your neck and then turn to the right until you feel tension on the left side. Your goal is to position your head at a point where there is no tension.
- Do the same with your back by bending forward and backward and then rotate your back to either side to establish the spot where there is no tension. Hold your back in that tension-free position. Your back should be long and relaxed.
- Make sure that your pelvis and hips are level. Stand for a moment. Relax the muscles of your back and abdomen and breathe deeply. Then balance your hips so that your right and left hips are even. Imagine your spine floating on your pelvis and continue to breathe deeply, feeling all residual tension drain away.
- With your neck long and your chin tucked slightly in, check your jaw muscles. This is a popular place to hold tension. Loosen your jaws with a quick tense-and-relax maneuver. Set your teeth slightly apart and make sure your tongue is heavy against the base of your mouth. You should feel your jaw muscles getting heavy and relaxed.
- Gently pull your shoulders back, and feel your chest open up. Now you should be able to breathe more freely and completely.
- Take a deep breath while bringing your shoulders up to your ears. Hold the breath and hold your shoulders there for a few seconds and then relax them. Check to see that the level of relaxation on each side is about equal. Try to ensure that both shoulders are at the same level and that one is not higher than the other. You may need to pull your shoulders up to your ears as you take deep breaths and let them drop a few times to get rid of any extra tension.

- Focus your attention on your abdomen. Locate your center of gravity, about two inches below your navel. As you breathe in, focus on that spot, and let all the muscles in your abdomen relax. Continue breathing consciously and feel your abdomen becoming calm and warm. You can incorporate abdominal breathing by pushing your belly out as you breathe in and pulling it in as you breathe out.

Jill was unable to shake off her latest bad cold. She couldn't get rid of the cough and she couldn't get her energy back.

After checking her lungs, her doctor said, "There's no sign of infection, but your posture is poor, your breathing is shallow, and your muscles are all tight. I'll make an appointment for you with a physiotherapist. She can show you how to open up your body so you can breathe and relax your muscles. You're all hunched and tight—you need to get loosened up and realigned so you're not in 'cough' position anymore."

Jill went to see the physiotherapist without high expectations and came out feeling like a new person. The therapist taught Jill how to open up her body by standing, sitting, and walking properly. She came away with her jaws and her neck relaxed, her head high, and her shoulders loose. Jill also got some pointers on how to walk and how to adjust her workspace to make it easier to maintain good posture.

QUICK PRESCRIPTION 21

Make the Adjustments

1) Balance your body by making sure that the left side and the right side of your head, shoulders, back, hips, and legs are about equal in the amount of tension that they hold.
2) Breathe consciously and let your muscles relax more and more with every exhalation.
3) Loosen your jaws.
4) Open your chest by bringing your shoulders back and taking deep breaths.
5) Make your shoulders broad and loose.
6) Relax your abdomen.

TAKE TIME OUT FOR EXERCISE OR PLAN TO TAKE TIME OUT FOR SICKNESS

If you are looking for a "magic bullet" to deal with stress, the one technique that I know you can rely on, even if you disregard all else in this book, is regular exercise. Exercise induces a state of inner calm and serenity and a feeling of balance between body and mind. If you work out often, you are teaching your body how to remain calm and balanced while you're under stress.

When I have an important speech to give, I always go for a workout at a certain time before the event so that I not only feel energized, but the resulting feelings of calm and confidence will be at their peak when I am about to speak. As you become more aware of how your body responds to exercise and how your energy flows during the day, you will be able to use exercise to program peak periods of confidence and inner cohesiveness when you need them most.

A further strategy I use to increase my stress resilience is to sit for a few moments after a workout, close my eyes, and breathe deeply. My goal is to feel all my muscles relaxing and my mind becoming quiet. I just keep my attention on the rhythm of my breathing and on my muscles becoming heavy and relaxed. This puts me in a state of calm readiness and it usually takes a lot to upset me after I have induced this level of balance and harmony in my body. Try it. The next time you work out, take a few moments to lie or sit quietly and breathe consciously and relax all your muscles. This will help you to build hardiness against stress.

If you are not too keen on exercise, hear this: your body has been built for action—it is a beautiful energy machine designed to take in fuel (food) and expend it in activity. If your body doesn't have enough to do, it will either store that energy (as body fat) or it will find ways to burn it off (through unnecessary muscle tension and physical tics and twitches) or both.

When you exercise, you are putting your body under stress. Stress chemicals, including cortisol and adrenaline, are released. You could say that exercise is a stressor because it triggers many of the same chemicals in your body that stress does. So why am I telling you to subject yourself to exercise? Because you can stop whenever you want to, and when you stop, your body learns to recover from the effects of these compounds. It's a way to develop hardiness against stress. Teaching your body how to recover from stress is an invaluable benefit that exercise can deliver.

Regular exercise also helps to transform your cells into economical users of energy. When you engage in vigorous physical exercise (brisk walking, running, cycling), your big muscles get most of the blood and oxygen; the other muscles and organs have to learn to manage on very little. At the end of the exercise session, your organs get flooded with oxygen-rich blood. Not only do you get a burst of energy at the end of the session, you're developing an energy-efficient machine. In general, people who exercise have more energy and feel less fatigue than those who don't.

This discussion about exercise is not about becoming a marathon runner or tackling a triathlon, although you're welcome to set those as personal goals if you'd like to. It is not about having to join a gym, or subjecting yourself to someone who behaves like a drill sergeant, nor is it about spending a lot of money on equipment or exercise clothes. It is about building physical activity into your life so your wonderful body has something to do with all that energy it's generating. And it's about conditioning your body so it will be able to recover quickly from a stress reaction.

If you are at all like the majority of my patients, you know that you should take time from your already busy schedule to condition your body so that it can withstand the rigors of stress, but acting on that knowledge is hard. The answer is to use a moment like this—what I call a moment of insight—to make a lifelong commitment to train your body in aerobic exercise for, say, half an hour every day. In addition to this definite training time, it is a good idea to include more exercise in your daily routine, such as walking up stairs or walking to the supermarket or parking a few blocks away from your destination to give yourself the gift of a short walk. Build your dedication to exercise in the knowledge that it will improve both your general health and your hardiness against stress. In a surprising way, exercise will reward you by giving back much more time than it took away from your schedule. Not only will your efficiency and life span tend to increase, but your happiness and vitality will as well.

Just to remind you why exercise is so important, here are some powerful motivators to encourage you to include more exercise in your life:

- Exercise will train your body to withstand stressful moments.
- Long-term exercise will help you recover more quickly from illness or injury.
- Exercise will increase your energy and reduce your feelings of fatigue.
- Exercise will elevate your mood and reduce feelings of depression by generating "feel good" hormones.
- Exercise will enhance your creativity. It causes asymmetric jerks in your brain and can trigger new ways of thinking. If you haven't already done so, try this some time: think of a problem and go for a run or a walk with it a few times and see what happens. Exercise has a positive effect on your memory and on brain function as a whole.
- Exercise will bolster your immune system and help you in your fight against tumors and viruses. It can retard the onset of diseases such as Type 2 diabetes, heart disease, and stroke.
- Exercise will help slow the aging process and eliminate many of the markers of age.

When you are under stress, be meticulous about sticking to

your exercise routine. It is an important time to practise relaxation exercises as well. In times like these, think of your body as being in a battle zone and be vigilant in protecting it from enemy fire.

Any plan to add exercise to your life must be an individual one and should be undertaken under the supervision of your family doctor to ensure that you begin an exercise program that is suitable to your current state of health and fitness. Regardless of the state of your fitness, you should check in with your doctor regularly, if only to monitor your blood pressure, heart rate, and blood fats.

If you've been inactive for a while, start very slowly, with modest goals. If you have been cleared for exercise, here are some general guidelines.

- Your goal will be to exercise on a daily basis for between 35 to 60 minutes—more intense exercise is usually done for a shorter period. If you aim to exercise daily and you miss once or twice in a week, you will still get the health benefits. Depending on your current level of fitness, you may need to start with something such as gentle walking. Be prepared to increase the intensity if the exercise becomes too easy.

- Choose an aerobic exercise—one that will build your heart muscle—that you like. Exercise is a lifelong commitment. Begin slowly and work up to a level of frequency and intensity that builds or maintains your stamina. Be prepared to try new things on a regular basis to keep yourself interested. Running, cycling, swimming, dancing, and brisk walking are excellent types of exercise that reduce stress. The rhythm of walking helps alleviate back pain, general anxiety, and tension. Choose the exercise that best suits your interests, your body, and your lifestyle. Your enjoyment of a particular form of aerobic exercise is a good indication of how often you will do it. I love to run. It is as if I am running toward happiness and running away from pain. This is my exercise—cheap, convenient, and independent. It can be done anywhere.

- You can choose to exercise any time of the day, but I find that it is easier to keep my commitment to daily exercise if I do it first thing in the morning. That way, it doesn't get lost in the pressures of the day and I reap the health-giving, stress-reducing benefits during the day.
- Make sure that you treat your muscles well. Do the appropriate stretching exercises. Stretch your back, thigh, and calf muscles before you do your core exercise program. I find it safer and better to stretch my muscles after five minutes of light aerobic activity, rather than doing stretching exercises when my muscles are cold. I also try to cool down with some stretches before I end the session.
- Whenever you feel tense or nervous, see if you can fit in a brief exercise session, even if you just go out for a short walk. If you are waiting to have a meeting and your counterpart is delayed, ask if you have fifteen or twenty minutes and use that time to go for a relaxing walk. You will be more effective when your contact finally arrives.

When Rick hit the basketball court for the regular Thursday pickup game, his buddies were amazed at his play. He challenged every opponent who had the ball, forced several turnovers, and managed some very long throws—a few of which even connected with the basket.

After the game, Gary said to him, "What got into you, man? You were unstoppable out there."

Rick said, "What a week! Monday, the computer system got a virus, then a major deal collapsed just before we were supposed to sign the contract, my second-in-command got sick and I've had to cover for him for three days, and to top it off, Nicole and I had an argument this morning—over nothing." He toweled off some sweat and caught his breath. "I really needed this game. A hot shower and an early night are going to make a big difference in the way I've been coping this week."

Gary grinned. "I wouldn't wish another week like that on you, pal, but you were the reason we beat the pants off those guys."

Rick laughed. "Yeah, it was fun, wasn't it?"

QUICK PRESCRIPTION 22

Rx

Exercise Your Options

1) Exercise according to your current state of health and fitness. Consult your family physician or a fitness professional before you start an exercise program if you've been inactive for a long time.

2) Choose exercise that you enjoy and a time and location that suits your schedule. Whether it's early morning, lunch, or early evening, it must be do-able.

3) Whenever you have some unexpected time—if, for example, a meeting is delayed or canceled—use the time to stretch or go for a walk instead of just going back to your desk immediately or waiting impatiently.

4) When you have to meet with someone, if it's appropriate, instead of meeting over coffee or going for lunch, go for a "walk and talk."

FUEL THE MACHINE

What you eat, how you eat, and when you eat all have an effect on your ability to master stress.

In times of stress, your body breaks down fat, carbohydrate, and protein to create energy for your response to whatever is troubling you. You will experience a rise in glucose, free fatty acids, and cholesterol in your bloodstream. Because of the increased glucose (sugar) circulating in your blood, your pancreas will secrete insulin. The insulin attack on the sugar in your blood will lead to low blood sugar levels, which means you'll experience feelings of irritability and nervousness, as well as hunger. This is a physiological stressor that stimulates your brain to secrete adrenaline and cortisol, raising your blood sugar again and rerunning the whole cycle of events until your body wears itself out.

If you reach for a quick snack to deal with the hunger pangs—perhaps some refined sugar to perk you up, or something satisfyingly fatty to comfort you—you will add to your stress reaction. That new food is quickly broken down and joins the sugar already in your bloodstream, which will require even more insulin. The result will be more feelings of irritability, more hunger, and eventual weight gain in addition to fatigue. This is how your food choices can affect the amount of stress you're feeling and your ability to deal with it.

Eating wisely is just another way to build hardiness against stress. Treat your body as a sensitive, dynamic entity that responds to what you put into it. (This is in fact what it is.) Eat only what you know will provide the best response. Just as you wouldn't consider putting anything but the best gas in your Mercedes, if you had one—it's a huge investment and it's important that it always be in good working order—don't plan to run the magnificent machine that is your body on anything less than optimum fuel.

When I talk to my patients, I find that most of them know how to eat properly. We all know what to consume and what to avoid, but we still don't eat very well. As with exercise, the problem lies in the will to practise what we know.

The key to nutritional success is your resolve, not your knowledge. Resolve right now to be prudent about what you eat and decide to stick to a good diet. Choose to eat foods that will make you feel well and perform well. Refuse to be self-indulgent. Stay away from refined sugar, dietary fat, and refined carbohydrates—just don't have them around. Eat more whole foods instead.

Don't let the way others eat influence you to eat badly. Don't let coworkers or family members convince you that your standards are too high and that you shouldn't be so picky about what you eat. Your decision is to develop a refined and integrated body and mind by fueling your system with the best you can afford.

That said, you ought to beware of special, restrictive diets that promise you the world in terms of health and anti-aging benefits. The fact is researchers are forever uncovering new evidence of what is good or not good. The best course is to live and eat wisely, paying special attention to the nutritional value of foods. If you follow the suggestions below, you will be using food to build mental and physiological toughness against stress.

Your goal is to have an optimal diet that will keep you looking young and feeling energetic, and at the same time protect you from disease. You may need to make a fresh start with a diet that is appropriate for your age and physical condition. Or you may just need to make some adjustments to a diet that is generally good, but tends to go off the rails in times of stress. Get some help with the details if you need to, but for most, a good diet is one that is rich in fiber and complex carbohydrates (such as vegetables, fruits, and whole grains). Avoid refined carbohydrates such as cakes, pies, and cookies.

A good diet is almost always low in fat (with little or no saturated fats from animal flesh or manufactured trans fat). Such a diet will contain protein that comes mostly from plants. The makeup of your diet should be about 65% of calories from complex carbohydrate, about 20% from dietary fat, and 15% from dietary protein. A high-fat diet is the enemy of your brain and heart, so beware of added grease and try to avoid fat in oils, meats, butter, and margarine. Don't let the taste of fat seduce you. Control your intake.

There is one type of fat called omega-3 or linoleic acid that is good for your cardiovascular system. You can get it from eating sardines, salmon, mackerel, walnuts, and ground flaxseed. Most of us don't get enough, so you should try to increase your intake of omega-3.

In addition, drink eight to ten glasses of water every day. A high percentage of your body is water. There is even some suggestion that your first hunger pangs are really a sign of dehydration and that you should start with a glass of water to make sure you are not taking in unnecessary calories. I try to drink three glasses of water in the morning before breakfast. Whenever I feel hungry, I first drink a glass of water. When I feel tired, I drink water and this has a rejuvenating effect on my energy.

There is anecdotal evidence that fresh juice from vegetables and fruits can help you detoxify some organs in your body. Many people swear by this practice and I have begun recommending juicing in general as a health protection measure, on an experimental basis. Many of my patients report that they feel more energetic and less stressed after a detoxifying routine of a few days. You may want to try different fruits and vegetables to see if juicing has benefits for you. At least fresh juice can help you avoid less nutritious foods. But don't forget that even if you're having fresh juice, you're still consuming calories.

As you try to fulfill your quota of daily fluids, be aware that coffee, tea, and colas, as well as other soft drinks containing caffeine, act as diuretics and will cause you to lose water. Coffee and tea may be your favorite beverages, but don't rely on them for hydration.

Time your eating so that your body gets a chance to do repair work while you're sleeping. This means no eating after 8 p.m. Your body should be able to finish digesting your meal before you go to sleep. Then it can use that time between 8 p.m. and before you break your fast to activate other hormone cycles and promote healing.

Part of your strategy to anticipate and plan for stressors should include planning a supportive diet for upcoming potentially stressful times. Nutritional foresight involves knowing where you are going in the course of your day, how long you will be there, what you will be doing, how hungry you are likely to get, and what temptations you will need to overcome. If you consider these factors, you can help yourself by preparing a plan of attack. Staying healthy involves work, but yields a multitude of benefits.

If you have to face a stressor, such as an exam or a big court case, recognize right away that you will be more vulnerable to illness, depression, interpersonal conflicts, and weight fluctuation, and take note. Awareness is a powerful weapon that can keep you from reaching for empty calories that weaken your immunity and your ability to handle stress. You should also avoid missing meals. I tell my patients not to be without an apple or some other fruit or some carrots just in case they're caught with no nutritional food in sight. Carrying your own fuel will eliminate the temptation to run to the nearest fast-food outlet and fill up on fat and refined carbohydrates, which will exaggerate any stress response. Keep an orange in the car. Carry water wherever you go and sip it all day long.

In addition to eating as well as you can, you may want to take a high-quality multivitamin and minerals supplement to protect yourself. Some experts claim that a healthy diet is all that's necessary; others contend that supplements should be added. If you don't think you're getting all the nutrients you need from the food you're eating, consider taking a supplement. There are many free radicals assaulting the cells in your body; if you can afford it, and experience no side effects, a multivitamin tablet with minerals may be a good protective agent.

The crew in the accounting department was gearing up for year-end, making plans for who'd deal with the auditors and how they'd get all the work done so the reports would be ready for the company's annual meeting. During the planning session, Beth, one of the younger staff members, spoke up. "I know this doesn't sound like it has much to do with year-end, but I was here last year and I'd like to make a suggestion."

"All suggestions are welcome," said the comptroller.

"Well, I hope you don't think I'm crazy, but . . . I know we have to work long hours and I don't mind that, but last year the staff fridge in

the kitchen was full of pop, and there's only junk food in the dispensing machine, and we always ordered in fried chicken. I gained about six pounds doing year-end last year and it took me forever to lose them. I was more tired and cranky than I thought I should have been, and a few of us were sick by the end."

"We always get sick by the time we're finished year-end," somebody said.

"Well, I was at a presentation by a nutritionist last week and I asked her what she thought we should do. She suggested we have lots of spring water and real fruit juice on hand, maybe some milk, and also keep a platter of chopped raw veggies, and low-fat dip for snacking. We could order in salads and sandwiches and get the occasional pizza. If you get the right toppings, they're not too bad. We could have some reasonably sized, low-fat bran muffins instead of cookies . . ."

Sheila, the bookkeeper, agreed. "That's a great idea. I didn't lose the weight I gained. I did some calculations based on last year and figured that if I did five more year-ends, I'll be the size of a bus!"

The comptroller was onside. "Beth, you're in charge of the food planning. One of our goals will be to finish year-end with everybody healthy and at the same weight we were when we started."

QUICK PRESCRIPTION 23

Rx

Eat to Build Resilience

1) Resolve to eat wisely every day. Be more conscious of what goes into your mouth.
2) Concentrate on eating complex carbohydrate and quality protein mostly from plant sources, and reducing your intake of fat.
3) Plan your eating in advance, particularly in challenging times.
4) Begin your new program of eating tomorrow and, for the next week, write down everything you eat. This will give you a chance to assess your true diet and enhance your discipline.

WHEN YOUR SIZE IS A PROBLEM

If stress or poor eating habits have already had an effect and you have gained weight, don't delay in taking action to get rid of those love handles or that potbelly. Remind yourself at every opportunity that fat around your middle is dangerous. It has been associated with the development of heart disease, hypertension, and cancer as well as the onset of Type 2 diabetes.

If you have a big weight problem and you don't think that you can deal with it on your own, talk to your doctor or a dietitian or nutritionist. There are many options open to you and there are even some medications that can help you jump-start the process of losing weight. Your family doctor has seen the consequences of too much weight expressed in terms of morbid obesity, hypertension, and general ill health and he or she can point you in the right direction. There is no miracle way to lose weight and keep it off—you need to slowly change your eating (and activity) patterns for life. The principles set out here are only the basics. If you need more information, it's time to consult a professional and your family doctor should be the starting point.

If you need to do something drastic to cut down your weight, plan your eating at least the day before. Write down the healthy food you will eat and the liquids you will consume and have those foods and drinks available. Don't buy foods full of empty calories—you can't eat it if it's not available.

Make use of your imagination in your fight against excess weight. Be proactive. Think about where you will be going and who you will be with. Visualize yourself facing the temptation to make an exception to your healthy choices and see yourself making (and enjoying) the right choices.

Keep lots of books and recipes about delicious, healthy eating handy so you can plan meals that you will enjoy. Then it will be easier to stick to your guns. I find that filling my mind with ideas about losing weight, looking young and vibrant, eating a diet for preventing diabetes and cancer, and eating to reduce my risk of heart disease and stroke keeps my motivation high.

In addition to the guidelines in the previous section, use the following six key words to remind you of what's important as you plan your meals. You can call it the F6 formula.

Frugal: The key nutritional strategy that will determine how long you live is how little you eat. We have given food all kinds of significance, linking it to celebrations, love, and comfort, but its primary role is fueling our bodies. While it is impossible to overfill your car's gas tank—the excess will spill onto the ground—our bodies have a very efficient fuel storage mechanism to keep that excess fuel with us in case we miss a fill-up. Therefore, eat only enough to fuel your immediate needs—everything else will go into unhealthy, stress-inducing storage. If you have a tendency to eat too much, use a smaller plate, or put smaller portions on your plate, and stay away from all-you-can-eat buffets.

One thing I find useful in my effort to control the amount I eat is to drink water before a meal. And I wait at least seven minutes before I decide to have seconds. By the end of that time, I usually find that the desire to take seconds has waned. I have also found that when I eat, it's best if I sit down to eat and do nothing else. This single-minded awareness helps me control the amount of food I consume. I also enjoy it more because I can savor the taste.

Frequent: Just because your goal is to eat less, this doesn't mean that you should miss meals. In fact research suggests that five or six small meals a day will supply you with optimal glucose (energy) levels and lower cholesterol levels. Plan to eat small amounts more frequently in order to avoid those blood sugar and insulin spikes. And those amounts should get smaller as the day—and your energy needs—wind down. "Eat like a king in the morning, a prince at noon, and a pauper at night" should be your motto.

For snacks, eat a piece of fruit or some raw vegetables

about mid-morning to keep your blood sugar close to the optimal level. You will handle the stressors in your life with greater ease and elegance. Take another fruit break in the middle of your afternoon. Actually stop working for a brief moment and concentrate on enjoying a fruit break. The practice of taking frequent breaks fits in well with the way your brain works. Your brain will rejoice every time you take a break, and will perform better for you after the break.

When you eat frequently, you won't be starving at the end of the day and you will be less inclined to pig out at a big meal or fall for some attractive empty calories that might beckon you from every corner as you head home.

Fortifying: Before you put anything in your mouth, think of nutritional content—vitamins, minerals, fiber, antioxidants, protein . . . Eat with awareness: before you eat anything, ask yourself if it will help you build resilience against stress and disease. If the food in question is just empty calories, like a piece of cake full of fat and refined carbohydrate, don't eat it. It is much better to throw it in the garbage than around your waist or your heart.

I used to look forward to meals mainly to entertain my cheeks. I never thought about food in terms of its contribution to my well-being or my performance during the day. Now, I eat mainly for the thrill of peak performance. Pleasure is secondary and I advise my patients to do the same so they can experience the excitement of feeling energetic and healthy.

Eating for pleasure and savoring the taste is great, but when you eat mainly for the pleasure of eating, the joy lasts only as long as the food does. The rewards of eating for health will last all day, all week, all month, all year, and even for a lifetime.

Don't fall for the old joke that everything that tastes good is bad for you. You may have developed a taste for sugar, fat, and salt, but let me assure you that, with a little practice, you can develop a taste for fresh fruit, crunchy vegetables, and herbs and spices.

If you choose the right foods (and I bet you know what the right foods are), the joy of eating will turn into a physical and mental lift that will accompany you moment by moment. You will sleep better and you will feel better all day long. Make food choices with this knowledge in mind. Choose foods that are packed with the stuff that enhances your health. Plan to eat foods that are fresh and when you eat, do so with the confidence that you are fortifying your body with the right nutrients.

Fruits and Vegetables: While fresh fruit and vegetable juices contain concentrated hits of some of the nutrients you need, eating the whole fruit or vegetable will give you the benefit of nutrients contained in the flesh and the skin, plus the increased amount of fiber. Regardless of your consumption of fresh juices, make sure you consume a variety of fresh fruits and vegetables every day. Carry some carrots, broccoli, celery, or other nutritious vegetables and fruits for lunch. Celery is a particularly good choice if you want to lower your blood pressure. These fruits and vegetables should be eaten in as close to their natural state as possible—avoid dips or cheese sauces on vegetables, or the ice cream or syrups that can come with fruit.

Fiber: When you plan to eat, think fiber. This means load up on fruits and vegetables. If the skin on fruits such as mangoes, apples, and peaches has been thoroughly washed, eat it. When you enjoy a baked potato, eat the skin. Your digestive system will thank you for it. Pay particular attention to this if you are over 50. (If your family has a history of colon disease, arrange for an examination as well. Colon cancer is one of the most preventable forms of cancer and it is a very common cause of premature death in North America.) Eating a high-fiber diet will help to keep your gastrointestinal tract healthy. An adequate amount of fiber will shorten the transit time of certain carcinogens and prevent them from being in contact with your colon long enough to cause harm.

Fasting: Occasionally you may want to try a juice fast in order to rest your bowel and detoxify your body, even for a day or two. Fasting has been credited with boosting memory and promoting clear thinking. An occasional water or juice fast using freshly squeezed juice from fruits and vegetables is one way to conduct a fast, but you may wish to do some research to find the method that suits you best, both physically and temperamentally. Consult a medical doctor if you decide to try this.

While fasting has been considered as a weight control measure, be aware that your body responds to "famines" by diligently storing fat once the famine's over, in case there's another one coming. Don't end a fast with a huge, fat-laden meal that will trigger weight gain. Nevertheless, fasting occasionally, if it works for you, is not at all a bad idea.

Jan was telling her sister about her latest weight problem. "I tried to get into those new pants I bought just two months ago and I couldn't get them zipped up!"

Her sister was sympathetic. "I've got some pants like that. I always figure I'll be able to get back into them soon so I keep them in the closet. What are you going to do?"

"Well," Jan said, "I think I have to make some serious changes in the way I deal with frustration. I was so mad when I couldn't get the pants done up that I ate a butter tart—it was frozen!"

The sisters both laughed. "That's not going to help!"

QUICK PRESCRIPTION 24

Rx

Cut Yourself Down to Size

1) Put the F6 formula into practice for the next 30 days: frugal, frequent, fortifying, fruits and vegetables, fiber, and fasting.

2) Drink water all day long. Water boosts brain power and improves cell communication.

3) Consult a health care professional if you need to make big changes. Work together to set an optimal weight goal that suits your body type. Eat for gradual, healthy weight loss and assume that the changes in your eating habits will last a lifetime.

IT'S NOT JUST BEAUTY SLEEP

When you pass by a school at recess, the schoolyard is lively with activity. You hear laughter and shouts of playfulness. You see dozens of kids in different groups: some playing with a ball, some locked in heated discussions, and some even singing. The school seems to reverberate with a sense of aliveness. You know that a lot is going on.

If you pass the school at another time of the day—when classes are in session—all is silent in the schoolyard. It is dead quiet and nothing seems to be happening, yet you know it is precisely then that the important business of the school is unfolding.

This scenario, according to Dr. William Dement, a specialist on the subject of sleep, is an apt analogy of how your brain works in wakefulness and in sleep. We tend to regard sleep as a non-activity. We should not, however, write off the time spent sleeping as a time when nothing important is going on. Sleep time is not dead time. Sleep is not the time that prepares you for the great work. Sleep *is* the great work. For your brain, this is the time when it is cleansing, nourishing, and organizing itself. For the rest of your body, this is a time to cleanse, nourish, and repair cells. Make sure that this time is effective.

We sleep 30% of our lives and yet many of us never learn to sleep properly. We often treat sleep as a necessary evil rather than as one of the best tools we have to ward off disease and improve our health.

During stressful times, your sleep is often disturbed and the much-needed inner work doesn't get done. You've probably noticed that after a long period of stress-induced sleep disturbance, you seem to look older, even haggard. This change is not your imagination. Sleep deprivation can accelerate aging as well as weaken your immune system. The good news is that you can reverse some of these effects if you can improve your sleep habits.

Don't just go to bed at night and hope you will be able to sleep well. Even if you don't have a problem sleeping, think about the importance of sleep and consider some of the following tips to enhance its value. These are practical ideas and techniques that will help you make the most of this very important part of your life, especially when some stressor is disturbing your life.

Go to sleep at about the same time each night and wake up at about the same time each morning, even on weekends. Seven hours a night feels right for most people. And don't rely on sleeping in on weekends to make up for regularly shortchanging yourself during the week. A daily habit of getting enough sleep is good for your brain and your body. If you are going through a challenging time, and you are tempted to cut down on sleep time, think again. Cut out something else. Proper sleep is essential to continued good health as well as great performance.

Keep business and other unrelated activities out of the bedroom—no computer and no TV. Reserve your bedroom for sleeping and sleeping only, perhaps with the exception of one other activity.

Deliberately prepare for sleep: as the time to go to bed gets closer, lower the light level to let your body know it's time to sleep. Switch from energizing sights and sounds to ones that are soothing. Avoid stimulating food and drink—especially those with sugar or caffeine. While the best idea is to avoid consuming anything after 8 p.m., if you must, eat complex carbohydrate. The digestion of these foods increases the availability of seratonin and tryptophan (a precursor of melatonin), both of which will help promote sleep. A glass of skim milk with low-fat, whole wheat bread or a bran muffin make an acceptable snack before bed for many of my patients who need the extra calories and the extra help. But eat only if you need the chemicals in the food to promote sleep.

As you prepare for sleep, beware of guilt, anger, hostility, a desire for revenge, fear, or worry that may be swirling in your mind and blocking sleep. Even if you are able to fall asleep, they will dominate your brain while it's trying to do its great work.

If you are plagued by these negative emotions, develop some ways of ridding yourself of them before bedtime. Try to create a special room in your head where you can go when you are ready to fall asleep. Leave your worries and fears in another part; bring only restful and positive thoughts, feelings, impulses, and images to this special part of your head. Lock the door and just let yourself be there with the beautiful feelings. Or create a "worry and anger" book: if you can't let go of negative thoughts and emotions, write them down in your book and then put the book away in a drawer for safekeeping. Tell yourself that in the morning, you will take out your book and take on all the worries again. Right now, it's time for sleep. Then create a relaxing atmosphere by acting and speaking calmly and lovingly. Reject any hostile thought, feeling, or attitude. Tell yourself firmly that the other stuff is all in the book, and that it can wait until tomorrow.

Consider using certain scents to promote relaxation prior to sleep, if you have no allergies or sensitivities to them. Experiment with them as you prepare yourself for relaxation and sleep. Lie on your back, breathe deeply and slowly, relax your muscles, and fill your bedroom with aromas such as rose, chamomile, lavender, or orange, or a mixture of them to create a feeling of relaxation; see what works for you.

As you go to bed, make it a habit to imagine all the tension in your body draining out through your heels, as you breathe slowly, and fully in and out. Feel the tension coming out of your scalp and face. Feel it moving out of your jaws, neck, and shoulders, flowing down through your back and abdomen, and draining out through an opening in both heels.

If you have a long-term problem with sleep, begin a regular, daily aerobic exercise program. Exercise promotes good sleep by helping to eliminate certain compounds that tend to make you anxious and tense. People who engage in vigorous, regular exercise tend to sleep well.

Beware of relying on pharmaceutical sleeping aids or alcohol to get you ready for sleep. If you use them regularly, you may not be able to fall asleep without them. Sleeping pills in particular, when used under the supervision of a medical doctor, do serve a useful purpose on a short-term basis, usually to get you through a bad period during a crisis. Just don't end up depending on them. It is better to struggle a bit to re-establish good sleep on your own than to take sleeping pills every night and end up dependent on them. Practise the relaxation exercise I outlined above instead. This can be just as effective as any pill and it produces better sleep without the possibility of unpleasant side effects.

If you have a sleep-related disorder or chronic insomnia, please see your doctor about it. There are sleep laboratories with sleep technicians and specialists who can help you. But start with your family doctor.

When Nazir's daughter was born, he took time off for paternity leave. The first Monday he was due back, his coworkers hung streamers in his workspace, and someone had thoughtfully placed a pillow on his desk with a sign that said, "Welcome to fatherhood!"

Nazir groaned when he saw the pillow. "I'm so tired, I feel like an old man. When I looked in the mirror this morning, I thought to myself, 'I expected to look more mature now that I'm a father, but this is ridiculous.' Look at me! I've got dark circles under my eyes, lines on my face. I look like a wreck. Neetha looks the same. The baby's fine, though—she's beautiful. It's just that she has a built-in detector that tells her to wake up whenever we fall asleep. We're hoping she'll get settled soon, and we can all get back to a regular sleep schedule. Tell me it gets better, Murray. Your kids are in high school, right?"

Murray snorted. "Don't count on things getting any easier, Naz. I was up until 2 a.m. Sunday morning waiting for a certain 17-year-old to come in from her night at the clubs."

QUICK PRESCRIPTION 25

Make Sleep Time Count

1) Establish and stick to a regular pattern of sleep.

2) When stressful times are underway, don't shortchange your sleep in order to catch up on other things. That is the time to build up your resistance to stress through proper sleep.

3) Regard your bedtime as the beginning of something important. Prepare for sleep deliberately—get your environment and yourself into a restful state.

4) As soon as you get into bed, clear your mind. Breathe in and out deeply and evenly; visualize and feel all the tension in your body draining out through your heels. Then tense all your muscles as you breathe in, and let them collapse with relaxation as you breathe out. It is good to do this while lying on your back so that you can practise abdominal breathing. Feel your belly rise as you breathe in and feel it fall as you breathe out.

RECLAIM YOUR ENERGY

NOTHING CAN DRAIN your energy like stress does. Muscle tension and hyperactivity are major symptoms of stress. A stress reaction can leave you feeling tired and worn out and often intellectually and emotionally numb as well.

If your energy is low, first rule out the possibility of disease. Many major diseases are silent and a little fatigue may be the harbinger of a major challenge to your health. Go for a physical checkup. Then take a hard look at the way you spend your day. How many hours do you spend at work? Do you engage in aerobic exercise at least four days a week? Are you eating too much? Are you consuming lots of refined carbohydrate and suffering from sugar blues? Are you getting enough sleep? Are you burning up hours in useless emotional turmoil? Are you worrying about your relationship or about money? Is stress the cause of your lack of energy?

As you know by now, effective antidotes to stress are exercise, a good diet low in refined sugar and fat, lots of fluids, a feeling that you are in control of your life, a firm commitment to doing something wonderful with your life, and love. These elements will also help combat fatigue.

Another technique for fighting fatigue is conscious relaxation. If you're clenching your jaws all day, tightening your neck and shoulders, continually straining to hear all that is going on around you, tensing your legs, or flexing your toes out of nervousness, you are wasting your energy in useless self-defeating activities. Instead learn to redirect that "activity" and release your muscles from their exhausting routine.

When you regularly practise relaxation exercises, your energy will soar. Once your muscles have been trained to relax, you can be relaxed "on demand"—any time you choose to be. You practise your golf swing and your tennis strokes because you want to improve your skills. Practise relaxing your muscles in a serious way for the same reason.

I am going to share with you four different techniques that you can use to train your muscles to give up their tension and stop using your precious energy to no avail. They will build on some of the skills you've already read about here and tried. Practise them frequently—separately or together—and you will reclaim the energy that you've been wasting by holding on to useless tension. When stressors come, you will be better able to withstand them.

The General Relaxation Exercise: Take three minutes to practise giving yourself the gift of relaxation in the morning and again in the evening. You can precede the exercise with a minute of abdominal breathing if you like. If you're not already practising this breathing technique, refer back to page 119 for a review. As you breathe in, say to yourself, "Breathing in, I observe my body and mind," and as you breathe out, say, "Breathing out, I smile and let all my muscles relax." Keep doing this as you allow a feeling of relaxation to flood all the muscles of your body.

Next, focus your attention on your toes, and say to yourself, "Toes relax"; then take another slow, deep breath and say, "Feet relax." Move systematically up your legs with every breath, relaxing your calves, knees, thighs, and moving right on up your body to your abdomen, your chest, and your shoulders, through your hands, arms, neck, and head. Concentrate on each area as you issue the instruction and feel the relaxation.

The 20-Second Instant Exercise: Take 20-second breaks several times during the day. Take a deep, slow breath and tense your muscles for a few seconds. Then relax as you breathe out. It is important to use your mind to feel relaxation coming into your body every time you exhale. Repeat this breathing, tensing, and relaxing three times and then continue to focus on breathing in and out, feeling a wave of relaxation coming over you every time you exhale. With practice you will be able to turn this simple technique into a highly effective stress buster.

Draining Tension Away Exercise: Imagine that your toes are removable stoppers screwed on to the end of your feet. Imagine your body as a bottle filled with tension. In your mind, unscrew your toes and visualize all the tension in your body flowing out through the openings in your feet. Give the tension a color if you like, and imagine this liquid tension draining out of your body. Let every drop of tension go. Feel it happening.

Screw your toes back on again. Imagine pouring golden, liquid relaxation into your body through an opening at the top of your head. See the liquid rise from your feet, filling up your legs; feel the relaxation as the liquid rises up your body. When the golden liquid has filled your head, your whole body will feel centered, balanced, and relaxed.

Whenever you feel that tension has taken over your body, just unplug your toes and let the tension drain out.

Awareness-of-Tension Exercise: I learned this awareness-of-tension exercise from Joel and Michelle Levey, authors of *The*

Fine Arts of Relaxation. It will help you to become so sensitive to the slightest onset of tension that your body will not have to shout in pain before you take note.

- First, tense your whole body as tightly as you can without hurting yourself. Respect any limitations that you have. Make tight fists with both hands. Tense your jaws, bring your shoulders up to your ears, and flex your ankles as if you want your toes to touch your shins. Tighten your abdomen and take a deep breath while you are doing this and hold it. Notice the tension. Then after a few moments, relax the tension and breathe out completely. Let every muscle in your entire body relax.

  Practise inducing deeper relaxation for a few moments by breathing in and out and allowing all your muscles to relax as you breathe out. Pay special attention to your out-breath. Try to become as deeply relaxed as possible as you exhale.

- Second, take a deep breath and tense your whole body half as much as you did the first time. Hold the breath and hold the tension. After a few moments, exhale and let all the tension go. Again induce deep relaxation by taking deep breaths and letting all your muscles go, relaxing them more and more with each breath.

- Third, tense all your muscles again, but this time, half as much as you did the second time. Pay special attention to this level of tension because this represents the amount of tension that you hold in your body most of the time. Note how your face, neck, hands, and legs feel with this little bit of tension in them. Now relax all your muscles completely.

- Get to know how a little bit of tension feels and whenever you feel yourself tensing up, deliberately tense some more and then relax completely. You will achieve a deeper level of relaxation by tensing and then relaxing than by just trying to relax.

Practise these four exercises several times a day. Since they are very simple exercises, you can do them all at one sitting or you can do one at a time. Don't just make a mental note to do a relaxation exercise whenever you think of it. It will not get done. Make it a priority to do these exercises three times during the day as training for your body.

You will notice that one of the exercises is very short—the 20-Second Instant Exercise. You can shorten it with practice so that it becomes an 11-second exercise. Just imagine being able to abort a stress reaction in 11 seconds!

Let's do the exercise right now as you read. Remember, this book is not about acquiring knowledge. It is about improving your physiology even as you read. Take a deep, slow breath and tense your muscles for a few seconds. Then relax as you breathe out. Use your mind to feel relaxation coming into your body every time you exhale. Repeat this tensing and relaxing three times and then continue to focus on breathing in and out, feeling a wave of relaxation coming over you every time you exhale. You have just practised an exercise that can reverse a stress reaction.

Post little reminders—in your kitchen, your office, your car, or on your computer—to do this instant exercise. Whenever you see one of these memory joggers—a sticker, a screen saver, a note, or a red dot or star on your watch—let it be a reminder to practise this instant exercise. Try to do this exercise all day long. Your goal is twofold: to release all the exhausting, pent-up tension that is wasting your energy, and to train your muscles and the rest of your body to relax at will.

One last, important note. A smile is an essential part of the exercises for creating relaxation. When doing any of the exercises, smile to yourself. Smile inwardly and outwardly if you don't mind looking happy when you are tense. Try to smile with your whole body. A smile has the power to change your physiology through its effect on your autonomic nervous system.

After months of uncertainty at the office, Morgan was exhausted. She told her mother, "I am so tired. The tension at work is nearly unbearable. The new project is late, some of our customers are canceling their orders, and layoff rumors are circulating all the time now. I've never dealt with anything like this before and my whole body feels like one big tuning fork—I'm sure if you poked me, I'd start vibrating. Doug says I should calm down, but I can't. I'm too pooped to go for a workout, or even for a walk, but I can't sleep either. I feel awful."

Her mother said, "You're going to have to take back your body, honey. You've let the tension at work invade your system and now it's running the show. Soak in a hot bath, for starters, to loosen up those muscles and practise your deep breathing. Then you've got to practise tensing and relaxing your muscles until you can be the one in charge again. Are you getting enough sleep? What are you eating?"

"Oh, Mother!" Morgan snapped, "I don't know which is more annoying. The fact that you're talking to me like I'm a kid again or the fact that you're right."

QUICK PRESCRIPTION 26

Do The Daily Anti-Stress Workout

1) Add a relaxation component to your regular physical workouts. After you exercise, just lie or sit and take deep breaths. As you breathe out, feel your muscles relax. Focus your attention on your breathing. Enjoy the calm, rejuvenating feelings of relaxation pouring into your muscles, and SMILE. SMILE WITH YOUR WHOLE BODY.

2) Practise the Instant Relaxation Exercise throughout your day: tense your muscles and breathe in, hold the tension briefly, then relax and breathe out. Smile and focus your attention on your arms and legs, and feel them becoming heavy and warm.

3) Do regular tension sweeps. If a particular muscle or group of muscles is tight, tense it some more as you breathe in, and then relax it.

4) Keep breathing and relaxing, focusing on your breath and your muscles throughout the day. End your day with one of the relaxation exercises. Drain away tension or practise tensing, relaxing, and breathing deeply as you prepare yourself for sleep.

PART FOUR

DEALING WITH THE KEY STRESSORS IN YOUR LIFE

"Life is just one {darn} thing after another."

—E.G. HUBBARD, 1909

WHEN I ASK my patients to tell me about the stressors in their lives, most of them talk about three sources. People tell me most often about constant change, never having enough time, and the fact that other people are driving them crazy. Let us deal with these key stressors one by one.

LEARN TO BENEFIT FROM CHANGE

IN THE OLD days, when change was not so continual, it used to be said that, "variety is the spice of life." Since then, it's been widely suggested that in the Western world more change has occurred in the last 50 years than in the previous 1,000 years. Now change, and the variety it brings with it, is not the spice of life; change is life itself. According to Peter Vaill, author of *Learning as a Way of Being*, we live in "a world of permanent white water." Sudden, unexpected changes and conflicting demands seem to be the order of the day.

If you intend to live your life well, you must develop a plan for dealing with change. If you don't, you will be bowled over by the changes that come your way and buffeted by the stress reaction that comes along as part of the package.

Since change is an unavoidable part of life, make the decision today to welcome it. This means that you're going to plan to benefit from change whenever it crosses your path. Don't think in terms of tolerating change or coping with change. Make up your mind that you are going to keep your eye out for change and benefit every time.

First and foremost, don't ever fight change, even when it is rudely imposed upon you. While it is easier to suffer, sulk, and complain, you will waste your energy and you will lose the fight. Just remember that change is inevitable. Accept the reality and work to profit from it. Whether the change is expected or comes as a surprise, regard it as a friend and resolve to benefit from it. This doesn't mean that your life will be easy, but it should ensure that you suffer less from stress.

We have a tendency to automatically think of change as loss. If a friend were to tell you that things have changed, you would immediately assume that something bad has happened—even before your friend had time to explain. If your spouse were to say to you, "There's been a change in plans," that's usually cause to resist the news and argue for what you were expecting. If your boss were to announce, "There are going to be some changes around here," it would be hard not to panic.

We usually fear change because we think that it will leave us worse off than we were before. We like what is familiar, especially when there is no disaster associated with it. As far as we're concerned, the unknown is full of potential disasters that we won't be able to control, so we adopt an attitude of fear. We forget that even if we are not the one who has chosen to make the change, we have the power to determine whether a change will make us better or worse off. For example, if the change is dismissal from your job, you can use the occasion to get another job and to profit more from your daily efforts.

Remember the critical role of perception whenever you are

faced with sudden and unexpected change. Perceive yourself as powerful and capable, and the situation as manageable. In the face of change, refuse to perceive yourself as a victim, no matter how big a wrench has been thrown into your day or your future. If you see yourself as a victim, your immune system, your endocrine system, and your cardiovascular system will begin to suffer as one change after another crosses your path. So never choose to think you are helpless in the face of the inevitable changes that will happen to you, even if you seem to have no control. Look at the change in the larger context of your purpose in life and ask yourself how you can use it to help you fulfill your purpose.

The second weapon in your arsenal against the stress of change is the knowledge that you can choose your response. You can decide to use a change in your circumstances to further your purpose in life, whatever the change may be or whenever it may strike. This is a crucial decision that will determine whether you go through life as a relaxed individual or a stressed-out, complaining victim. Every hardship or opposition has the potential to make you better and stronger. Don't miss out on these gifts for self-improvement that are brought to you by change.

Decide now that whenever you must respond to a change, you will spend your time and energy only on efforts that will help that change to put you in a better position than you were in before. Don't mope. Don't blame. Don't prophesy catastrophe. Don't indulge in self-pity. This takes energy and you might as well use the energy to arrange your life so that you will reap those benefits that may be hidden in the change.

Develop a resolute and positive disposition as far as change is concerned. If you resolve to benefit from any change that touches your life, you will become mentally strong and the changes that come with modern life will only enrich your journey. Remember that the real secret of success is not what happens outside but what happens inside—in your thoughts, in your immune system, in your energy level, and in your sense of confidence and strength. You can control all these factors.

Remember, when a man has a hammer, everything looks like a nail. When you are intent on seeing only opportunity, that is what you will see and adversity becomes a stranger to you. Recognize change as an inspiration for creating a better life.

Enlist all the help you can get, including your finest intellectual effort, in order to turn a potentially negative event into a benefit. Give yourself time to examine the potential of the change instead of automatically assuming that disaster is about to darken your future. Use some of the following questions to analyze a change before you make a decision about how to handle it:

- Who's initiating the change and who exactly is it affecting?
- What aspects of your life will be affected, and what aspects won't be affected?
- Why is the change happening?
- Where will the effects be most apparent?
- When will the change take place?
- How will the change affect your goals in life and what's important to you? How can you use the circumstances to spark positive energy in the rest of your life? How can you restrict any negative influences?

Jamie had been starting his day by exercising at a gym on his way to work for the past few years and had gotten into a comfortable routine. The workouts made him feel good, he'd lost some weight, and the timing suited his schedule. That was about to change.

He received a notice in the mail that the facility he belonged to would be closing in a few months. The company that ran the chain had just done an expensive refurbishment of a club a few blocks away. When it reopened, Jamie's would close. The company had offered some options to current members—they could switch to the new facility, go to another club in the chain, or get a refund on their membership and go elsewhere.

Pete was in the dressing room when Jamie arrived the next morning and he asked Jamie what he thought he might do. Jamie said, "I talked to my wife about it last night and I found out she's interested in joining a gym—she just didn't want to come here because it was so run-down. We're going to look for another gym on the way to work, and I'm hoping she'll join me in the morning workout routine. What about you?"

Pete said, "My company relocated about six months ago. I could find something closer to the new office. On the other hand, this is close to home and the new facility looks like it will be pretty state-of-the-art. There will be a bigger variety of equipment, and your wife's right about this place . . . it would be nice to be somewhere that's a bit cleaner and classier. Have you talked to Ed yet?"

Jamie grinned. "What was he upset about a couple of weeks ago? They changed the location of the photocopier on his floor? He went on about that for three days. This should be good."

Just then, Ed walked in. His face was red. "Did you get that notice?" he demanded. "They can't close this club. I've been coming here for fifteen years! It's the way I start my day—I can't change that. I'm going to start a petition and stop this. It's a disgrace the way they think they can push us around!"

Jamie and Pete exchanged winks and headed out to the weight room.

QUICK PRESCRIPTION 27

Sail with the Winds of Change

1) Make up your mind that you will always welcome and benefit from change. This means that you will suffer less stress and achieve greater success, but it does not mean your life will be easy.

2) Focus your thoughts and your energy on finding ways in which you can benefit from the new circumstances. Will the change make it easier or more difficult to achieve your goals?

3) Evaluate the change in light of your purpose. Can you create new goals that are more worthy than the ones you had aspired to before?

4) Take the opportunity to do some thinking and be clear about what you want to do with your life. Ask yourself, "What do I really want to get out of my life and how will this change help me get it?"

PRESSED FOR TIME

Earlier I said that the best definition of life I'd heard was that "Life is one darn thing after another." A second definition of life that appeals to me comes from the Bible: "What is your life? It is a vapor that appears for a little time, and then vanishes." No one these days would challenge the truth of that statement. The "vapor" that is characterized by the passage of time seems to be disappearing even faster than it did a few years ago. Many of my patients seem caught in a time squeeze and suffer "hurry sickness" over what they perceive as their failure to accomplish the many things they have to do in the amount of time they have every day. They are often overwhelmed by constant feelings of urgency and of being behind.

The truth is that none of us gets more than 24 hours in a day, regardless of how important we are, how many people depend on us, or how much we multitask in an effort to get more done. My patients speak of "to-do" lists that never get any shorter and working long into the night to finish tasks at work or at home. They have voicemail messages gathering at different phones, and e-mail messages that multiply in their e-mail boxes. They feel worried and guilty about the things that didn't get done, and lie awake at night worrying about how to do everything that must be done the next day.

As they become anxious about the demands on their time, they suffer the health consequences of their perception that they are unable to cope with it all. Their anxiety makes them respond to everything in an agitated or exaggerated way because they are always on high alert. Relationships are neglected. Concentration is impossible. Feelings of helplessness, fatigue, and unhappiness become constants in life.

How can you deal with the time pressures in your life?

Choose to leave room in your life for living. Don't play the victim at work or at home. Don't let anyone trick you into being a machine programmed to respond to every call and every demand. It is OK to miss a call or two. It is OK to ask—or hire—someone else to do some of the work. It is OK to call a family meeting to help decide what is important and how those important things will get done. It is OK to decide that some things don't need to be done at all. The real question is, "Are you happy and fulfilled?"

Remember that life is about happiness, and happy people add greater value to their work, their families, and to society.

Every day, leave a margin for doing the things that rejuvenate your energy. In other words, create space in your life. Begin to create free time for yourself. Plan to begin each day with ten minutes for yourself. Reflect on the person you are, why you are here, and think about your relationship with the rest of the world's beings. Don't think about what you have to do. Don't think of yourself as a computer programmer, a lawyer, a nurse, a secretary, a manager, a mother, or a father—forget all those labels you have been given. Just be a human being. Use some of that early morning time to appreciate the beauty of nature. This practice is particularly important when you're overloaded with too many things to do.

Do the same at the end of your day—leave some time and energy to play and to give love and thanks. Don't drain all the energy you have into your work and housekeeping activities.

Don't work all your waking hours. Leave another margin so you can cater to yourself and the people who love and support you. The purpose of life is to enjoy it.

During the day, don't schedule yourself so tightly that you have no time to pause and be yourself. Leave little margins in between activities—create Sabbaths in your day. People who do this accomplish more.

Every time the phone rings, use the sound as a cue to take two deep breaths and relax your muscles. Answer on the third ring. Use all the little signals that prompt you to begin a new task as cues to relax, breathe, and slow down to gain control over your body and mind. Treat waiting between activities as a gift to your heart and your brain. When you approach your tasks think quality, not quantity. Put the stamp of excellence on everything you do by bringing the full weight of your attention and focus upon it. Try doing just one or two things well every day. You will do less. But you will get more done. You will have more power. You will be more connected. That is the secret of personal effectiveness.

By the time Karen and Don's kids were in high school, they both had management positions in large corporations. They both put in long hours and had to travel for work. Countless meetings, stacks of e-mail and voicemail, reports, and reorganizations were the order of the day at work. At home, there was more voicemail and e-mail, plus snail mail, hurried chats with family, clutter everywhere, and a mad scramble when there was a special event.

One night as Karen passed the living room, she tried to remember the last time she'd actually sat for a few minutes on the couch. A few days later, around 1 a.m., while the last load of laundry finished in the dryer, she found herself staring into a fridge that contained a number of dangerous-looking things. She sent an e-mail asking for a family meeting to discuss household chores that weekend.

Her 16-year-old daughter sent this reply, "We keep having these meetings, and you keep assigning us jobs, and then you get mad and do it yourself because you don't like the way we stack the laundry or something. It's a waste of time, and I have a practice on Saturday. I'm not coming."

Karen was furious; Don tried to mediate.

"You're going to have to decide what matters and what really doesn't as far as the house is concerned. Obviously, we don't want anyone to die from eating something that's been in the fridge too long. Maybe whether the blue towels and the blue facecloths are stored together in the linen closet is less important. As a family, we're going to have to decide what we have time for and what we don't. I would like to have dinner together once in a while. On the other hand, I'm going to cancel the magazines that I don't have time to read, and I'm resigning from the library board. I can't make it to the meetings and I'm not helping their cause. Let's face it, Karen. There's too much to do and we're starting to lose control. I'm really sorry I missed our anniversary."

Karen looked at him blankly. "Good grief," she said, "so did I."

QUICK PRESCRIPTION 28

Master Your Time Pressures

1) Spend ten minutes in the morning with your eyes closed, and induce a sensation of deep harmony in your body and mind. You can use the General Relaxation Exercise on page 150 or the Awareness-of-Tension Exercise on page 152 to create the feeling.

2) Review your purpose in life. Get your priorities straight as you plan your day with your purpose in mind. Choose the three, not four (maybe even two), things that you want to accomplish today and focus on them.

3) Begin your day with a heart full of appreciation and gratitude, no matter what the coming day looks like or how grave you think your troubles might be. Plan to go through your day with thoughts and attitudes of thankfulness.

4) Take note of the people who are important in your life and resolve not to ignore them.

5) During the day, experience the incredible lightness of a pause—more than once. Use the 20-second Instant Exercise regularly to train your body to relax.

WHEN IT'S PEOPLE YOU CAN'T STAND

MOST STRESSORS COME on two feet and talk back at you. To quote Jean-Paul Sartre, "Hell is other people." If you are going to reduce the tendency of stressful events to upset your health, you will have to learn to deal with difficult people and difficult interpersonal relationships. Now is a good time to resolve that you will never allow other people's behavior toward you to affect your health.

There are almost as many theories about why obnoxious people behave the way they do as there are obnoxious people. Some believe that when we are miserable, we tend to resent the fact that other people are happy and we try to make them a part of our misery. Or, I'm sure you have heard the idea that everything we do in life is either to get love and approval or to make up for the lack of it. If you understand this as a motivation behind destructive behavior, you will be better equipped to handle interpersonal stressors.

Sometimes, the obnoxious person you are dealing with just had a very unpleasant experience and cannot help but pass it on. You are finding out first-hand how an unpleasant experience can trigger negative emotions that ripple through a day and touch many others.

You can eliminate a lot of stress from your life if you resolve never to let the way other people treat you determine how you will treat them. Don't let negativity dictate your behavior. If the stressor is an unwarranted insult, don't feel obliged to return the favor. Treat other people according to the principles and values that are important to you, and always try to counter the negative with a positive. Learn to respond to unpleasantness with a pleasant and agreeable attitude. In other words, make it a given that you will always try to overcome nastiness with good humor.

Consider looking for the humanity in every human heart. The deeper you look inside yourself, the more you see how much we are all alike. Remember that, given the pressures, circumstances, and the resources available at the time, most of us are doing the best we can. Sometimes we look back over our day and must admit that we made a poor showing—but it was the best we could manage. We need to forgive ourselves and resolve to move forward. We need to do the same for others. This compassion can help when you're dealing with negative behavior.

When you are the target of a verbal attack, remember not to get caught up in the behavior. Back away from conflicts and unnecessary fights. If a conflict already exists, you have to deal with it, but learn to spot conflicts before they worsen and back away from them. There are enough essential fights to sap your energy. Therefore, preserve your strength. When someone calls you a fool, agree, and move on in peace. Don't give him or her any of your strength. Remind yourself of what is important to you and who is important to you. Don't waste a precious hour—or even a minute—getting tense and fuming over a slight from someone you don't know and who doesn't know you, and then waste the rest of your day regretting what you did or didn't say. Just back away from the whole thing and save what is important—your energy and your health. Some people seem to cross your path just to test you, to see if you have the strength to turn away from their pettiness.

A crucial part of this business of backing away from conflicts and anger is to turn to the key emotions that we talked about before—gratitude, hope, confidence, enthusiasm, compassion, joy, love, and inner peace and harmony. Remember these positive emotions. Choose to fill your head with them so there is no room to entertain anger, jealousy, fear, resentment, or the like. Nurture these positive emotions all the time. Meditate on them, talk about them, and try to emulate them wherever you are and whatever you are doing.

If it seems as if negative emotions cannot be avoided, step aside (even if you can do it only in your mind) and quietly let the unpleasant feelings pass by without touching you. If someone throws some raging anger your way, actually lean back and let the anger pass by you. Refuse to catch any negative emotions when they are thrown at you. Practise this action in your mind and, if you can, actually do it with your body.

How else do you deal with those stressors on two feet? According to that pragmatic philosopher William James, "The art of being wise is the art of knowing what to overlook." You will decrease the stress in your life if you learn to overlook some of the irritations and stressors that come your way. Don't feel you have to notice and correct everything that you perceive as being wrong in the universe. You don't have time. Learn to overlook some mistakes. Ignore some wrongs. If someone steps on your toes, it might be in your best interests, this time, just to overlook it. Don't rise up against all the annoyances that you encounter. Overlook some of them. No justification, no rationalization. Just overlook them for health's sake and move on.

If you're a parent, don't wear yourself out correcting every perceived flaw that you see in your children. Overlook some, but correct the important ones. If you're in a relationship, cut your partner some slack; do the same for your supervisor and coworkers. This does not mean you should lower your standards or abandon your values and become a doormat, but it does mean that you need to let those around you be themselves and live their lives and achieve their goals in their own way.

Beyond the understanding, the overlooking, and the compassion, be aware that some people are just obnoxious. Why this is so may be a mystery to you—one that you may never solve. Or you may know the reason. Nevertheless, the attitudes and behaviors of these people are stressors and have the potential to drain your energy and upset you to the point where you can become seriously sick. I can't tell you how many patients I have seen whose migraine attacks, irritable bowel pain, hypertension, irregular heart rates, depression, and nervousness are due to the unreasonable behavior of another.

When dealing with someone who is difficult and obnoxious, guard your body, mind, and spirit. That may include minimizing the amount of time you spend with the person. It is also a good time to practise your breathing exercises and pay attention to your muscles instead of attending to your tormenter.

It is natural for us to feel hostile, frustrated, and resentful at times. Instead, remember that you can choose how you respond to obnoxious people. Choose to turn their negativity aside and be grateful that you are able to do so.

Tom is a doctor with a varied family practice. One afternoon, as he was standing at the receptionist's desk reviewing some patient files, one of his regulars, a wheelchair-bound elderly man with a cranky disposition, came into the office. As soon as he spotted Tom, he launched into his tirade. In a loud, angry voice he said, "Doctor, your pills are no darn good. I've been taking them for two weeks, and I still have the cough. What kind of doctor are you if you can't help a patient?"

Tom took a deep breath and asked himself if he would let this man undermine his confidence and ruin his day. Instead of seeing him as a threat, Tom looked again and saw a frail and frustrated man who struggled with health problems, mostly caused by his refusal to quit smoking. Now was not the time to resume that discussion.

"I totally agree with you," he said. "Sometimes when we prescribe these pills, they don't work. That must be frustrating for you. It's a good thing that you've come in to let me know there's still a problem."

The man was so taken aback by Tom's attitude that he lowered his voice and said, "Doctor, I know you are the best I have ever had. I just want to know if I should double the dose or get something else."

That man was so impressed by Tom's way of handling the stressor he'd dished out that he became a major source of referrals to his practice.

QUICK PRESCRIPTION 29

Reduce Stress from Other People

1) Resolve to overlook others' flaws and mistakes.
2) Choose your battles with care and make sure they are well worth your energy.
3) Be aware of obnoxious people—there is nothing you can do to change them. You can only take care of yourself.
4) Remember your positive emotions—gratitude, hope, confidence, enthusiasm, compassion, joy, love, and inner peace and harmony. Fill your day with them. Emulate them in all your actions and notice them with joy when they appear in others.

WHEN YOU ARE THE PROBLEM

SOMETIMES NOT ALL of your stressors are external—everything around you is proceeding as it should. The only problem is you. Your ego has taken center stage and you're taking everything that happens personally. You're locked in "worry mode," you're afraid, you're just in a lousy mood, or you're depressed. You must have a plan to deal with these times as well. Otherwise you will not only feel stressed unnecessarily, you run the risk of becoming a big source of stress in the lives of everyone around you.

Just to review, thoughts originate in your brain and feelings and emotions are connected to your brain's limbic system. The pre-cortex area in your brain that controls your actions is connected to your limbic system. If you change your thoughts, you can influence the way you feel and the way you act. The discussion and prescriptions that follow will help you change your thoughts when your ego, your worries and fears, your mood, or mild depression are starting to run away with you.

Before I deal with the specifics, however, I would like to remind you of some previous points and techniques that are relevant here.

- You can make choices—you are not a prisoner of your moods and emotions.
- You can change your physical and biochemical state by moving your body—yes, going for a workout. Even better, the next time you are in a funk, exercise right there in your house or

apartment for 12 minutes, or try getting out and going for a short walk. A really good idea is to put on some lively music and get up and dance for 12 minutes.

- You can do the Instant Relaxation Exercise as soon as you feel yourself being caught up in a web of negative emotions. Use your negative feelings and situations as cues to practise inducing physiological harmony. Use the acronym **T.A.B.S.** to remind yourself of the steps in Quick Prescription 10:
    - **T**ense and relax your muscles for a few seconds
    - **A**rms and legs become heavy and warm
    - **B**reathe deeply and evenly
    - **S**mile and relax your body

When a bad mood or negative emotions predominate, and you are feeling lousy, remember to ask yourself how you would like to feel. Then imagine how you would act, think, or behave if you felt that way. Begin to act, think, and behave in a way that matches how you would like to feel.

CUT YOUR EGO DOWN TO SIZE

Do you notice any of the following: everything that happens is a disaster designed to make your life more difficult; no one could possibly understand your problems; no one else can do anything properly; or even the good things that happen aren't good enough to satisfy your standards? If you do, it's time to shift the center of the universe. Move away from the tendency to inflate your importance. See yourself as a channel for the blessings and benefits of life to flow to others.

Do you ever find yourself interrupting, criticizing, showing off your knowledge, or trying to steal center stage when it's not your turn to be there? Don't keep people from having their own chance to shine and receive the credit that is their due. Don't be so intent on letting people know how great you are that you prevent them from getting their own jobs done, or seeing and appreciating what is really important. Don't assume that everything must be set up to satisfy your situation and particular needs. Be flexible enough to let things be for the common good of the greatest number of people.

The staff at the clinic was waiting for "Mr. Big," as they called him. He arrived at the appointed time, strode to the front desk, and made a show of checking his Rolex to note the time.

"I'm here to see Dr. Crawley. I assume you know who I am."

The receptionist was ready for him. "That's fine. The doctor is just finishing up with his previous patient and he'll be with you in a moment or two. If you'll just take a seat . . ."

"Excuse me," "Mr. Big" cut in. "My appointment is for now. Perhaps you don't know *who I am. My time is very valuable."*

The other patients in the waiting room stiffened slightly at the announcement and exchanged glances. "As if no one else's is," one of them muttered.

"I never allow my staff to keep me waiting. I run a major corporation. If I carried on the way you medical people do, the economy of this country would suffer. I've half a mind to send some of my people in to help you sort out this practice. In fact the whole medical industry would probably benefit from my administrative expertise."

Dr. Crawley arrived just then. "If you'll just come into this examining room here . . ."

"I don't need an examination, Doctor. I know what's wrong with me."

The staff could hear the patient's voice rumbling through the door as he met with his doctor. The appointment went overtime as the physician attempted to make a diagnosis. As the man left, the receptionist asked him if he needed to book another appointment.

"I don't have time to do that!" he snapped. "I'll have my secretary call you."

As the door swung shut, Dr. Crawley's partner winked and said to him, "And what did the great man have to say today?"

"I honestly don't know why he comes in. He self-diagnoses. He's got to be spending time reading medical texts—you should hear the jargon he uses. He lectures me. And he doesn't want to hear my opinion. It's the same problem that it always is: he's got to cut down on his high-living lifestyle before it kills him. But it would probably ruin his image if he drank spring water and ate some salads. I can only hope that he survives his first heart attack. Then maybe he'll listen."

"Well," said the receptionist, "we can at least be grateful that he comes in here only a couple of times a year. Think of the poor people who have to deal with him every day. What a nightmare that must be!"

QUICK PRESCRIPTION 30

Rein in Your Ego

1) Remind yourself that the sun is the center of the universe, not you.
2) If you have a choice between boosting your own ego or boosting the ego of others, boost the ego of others.
3) Accept the fact that other people have standards, practices, and opinions that may differ from yours, but they are still valid.
4) Resolve never to get in the way of other people being themselves.

THAT'S JUST ME, I'M A WORRIER

One day I asked a group of patients to describe their experience of worry. I emphasized that the first thought that came to mind would suffice.

Here are some of the responses:

- "Worry is useless and non-productive. It's like a rocking chair; it gives you something to do, but gets you nowhere."
- "Worry makes you live in the future; you miss the joy of the present."

- "Most of what you worry about never happens." (This is true: According to research, 96% of what we worry about never happens or is downright irrelevant.)
- "'I am worried about you' is like a badge some people wear all their lives, as if worrying is a sign of a noble heart."

And yet we worry.

The next time you are in an agony of worry, first relax your body. Use **T.A.B.S.** (see page 177) to calm your muscles and your mind will follow suit.

Then ask yourself what exactly it is that you are worried about. Get to the root of it. Identify the part of the situation that is most disturbing to you. Filter out all the side issues and get to the core.

Once you've identified the cause of your worry, ask yourself what would be the worst thing that could happen. "Will I die? Will I lose my family? Will I lose my vision? Will I lose my job? Yes, I could lose my job. Well, how bad is that?" Remember your resolve to deal with change by finding a way to turn it to your advantage: "The fact is, I always wondered if I should be doing something else and if I lose my job, it will be a good time to find out what my calling really is. So it's not too bad after all."

Once you've identified the worst possible outcome, go to work to prevent it from happening or to minimize the stress that it is likely to produce. Face the circumstances. Rehearse the steps that you need to take to deal with the situation and make yourself triumph over it in case your worry is one of the 4% of things that do actually happen. Write down your plan and put it in a safe place. Then get on with your life.

Lynn had just started lunch in the staff room when the woman next to her nudged her.

"There's Stacy," Barb whispered. "Honest to God, I don't know how she does it."

"Does what?"

"Just manages to get up every day. She's had cancer, you know. I'm so worried about getting cancer. Last night, I thought about getting cancer, and not seeing my kids graduate and get married or seeing any of their babies. I cried for an hour."

"Barb, is there cancer in your family?"

"Not yet."

Lynn looked at her very carefully. "Do you have any symptoms?"

"No, but it's a common enough disease," Barb said defensively. "We've all seen the statistics."

Lani spoke up. "I was awake all last night thinking about what would happen to us if Neil lost his job. Don't you look at me like that either. It could happen. We've got a lot of debt right now and it would be a disaster! Just because he's got seniority and his industry's growing and his company's one of the best doesn't mean . . ."

At this point, Diane cut in. "I personally am very concerned that there's going to be an alien invasion. I think hordes of them are going to land and go straight to the shopping malls. They will be disguised as security staff and by the time we notice that they all have green faces, it will be too late! They will have snapped up all the toilet paper and whisked it off to another galaxy. My family will be desperate. Our civilization will be brought to its knees! But," she winked at Lynn, "I'm not going to lose any sleep over it."

The other two were offended. "Oh, you!"

QUICK PRESCRIPTION 31

End Needless Worry

1) When a particular worry dominates your thoughts, say out loud or in your head the word "Stop," and visualize a red light coming on. Keep doing this until you have regained control of your thoughts.
2) Identify the specific thing that is eating away at you. Write it down. Then ask yourself, "What's important now? What do I have to do right now?" Get busy doing it.
3) Fill your mind with your choice of positive emotions. Begin by thinking about these positive emotions and imagine that you are so full of these wonderful emotions that they are overflowing into your attitudes and actions and there is no room for any other sentiment.

PARALYZED BY FEAR?

Fear is a strong negative emotion. Its negative energy often helps you turn negative events into disasters through your actions (or inaction). Fear affects not only your mental health, but your physical health as well, in ways that we are often very aware of.

When you find yourself caught up in a web of fear, there are certain steps that you can take to set yourself free from the paralyzing influence of this emotion. First, recognize the emotion. Call it by its name, and acknowledge that you're caught in the clutches of fear. Simply know what it feels like. Next, meet the fear, lean into it. Recognize what it's doing to you. Know which parts of your body it is affecting: your stomach, your chest muscles, deep inside your heart, your back. Locate the part or parts of your body where the emotions are having an effect.

Next, establish control over your body. Don't let fear determine your posture or facial expression. As soon as you recognize what it is doing to you, take control of yourself. Begin with your body. Do the **T.A.B.S.** exercise to establish physical control:

- **T**ense and relax your muscles for a few seconds
- **A**rms and legs become heavy and warm
- **B**reathe deeply and evenly
- **S**mile and relax your body

Keep doing this as long as you need to. Fear often has a disturbing physical effect, so you need to regain control.

After you have re-established physical control, try to induce a state of calm by continuing to breathe fully and consciously, and feeling your mind becoming still. If a particular fear keeps occupying your mind, use the red light technique described to stop worry. Order yourself to "Stop" and turn on the red light. When you regain your mental composure, ask yourself, "What is the real cause of my fear?" Then, if you want to triumph over fear, decide that you will act with courage despite the presence of fear.

The key, as always, is to be aware and to refuse to be a victim. Don't passively accept the feeling; dissect the emotion and see where it's coming from. When the situation seems overwhelming, break it down into its component parts. Find the part in the whole package that is most upsetting to you. For example, you may think you fear a divorce. First ask yourself what part of the whole situation is really bothering you. What is keeping you from sleeping? Is it that you may be forced to sell your house? Do you fear a loss of status or a change in lifestyle? Are you afraid of the impact on your children? Find out the underlying cause of your emotional dilemma and what it has to teach you. Work on the things you have identified and separated from your more general fear. Be prepared to learn.

Listen carefully to what you are telling yourself as you experience your particular fear. Is your "self talk" making you stronger or is it making the fear stronger? You can change the tone and course of your internal conversation. Again, use your skills in emotional redirection to assume the role of a courageous person. Ask yourself, "If I were full of courage and felt no fear, how would I feel? What would I be thinking? How would I act?" Act the part of a person without fear, and the fear will dwindle. Take yourself in the direction of your most positive and powerful thoughts.

Do what you know you have to do to succeed in the situation. You may have to call your spouse to discuss the impending divorce. Take action in the presence of fear. The difference between the courageous person and the fearful person is that while they both feel fear, the courageous person takes action despite his or her feelings.

Lastly, fill your mind with those positive emotions that we have repeated so often. Let them overflow from your body and mind: gratitude, hope, joy, relaxation, compassion, confidence, and love. Act with these emotions in mind.

At 3 a.m. Jackie got up and went into another room. The baby was scheduled for a battery of tests that day and the waiting was torture. She and Rob both knew that there was something wrong with their youngest child. She wasn't responding the way the other two had; she seemed to be behind in her development in almost every way. It had taken months to get the tests set up, but the fear of what the doctors would find was overwhelming.

In a few minutes, her husband joined her.

"Rob, I am so scared. The possibilities they've talked about . . . some of them sound so awful. I don't know how I'm going to get through the next few weeks of tests and waiting for results."

"I know what you mean. We have an idea of the worst it could be and it's hard to think about anything else. But knowing has got to be better than not knowing. What are the issues here? Our pride in our ability to produce a healthy child? Our picture of our perfect lives? Our coming dependence on a bunch of unknowns? And we've got two other kids who need us. We can't let them get lost in this. We have to keep reminding ourselves that we're good parents, and we're resourceful."

"Yes. Yes, we are. I have to get these 'night terrors' under control so I can sleep and not be so on edge. Lots of other people have been down this road before us, and they've managed. I'll just have to pretend I'm one of them."

"You will be one of them, sweetheart, and so will I. I admit I'm saying that with more confidence than I feel. We can only deal with the moment—we can't deal with the things we don't know about yet. Let's shrink this monster to what we can deal with right now, and take it a bit at a time. Today it's the tests and that's all. They're going to be scary for such a little one."

"I know! Needles and tubes—she'll have no idea what's going on . . . I can be there and make her as comfortable as I can. I am going to put on a courageous act and present myself as a champion mom to help keep her calm. For the rest, I've got to slam the door on all that scary stuff and

deal with what's right in front of me. I can be grateful for the help we're getting and hopeful about the future and that's about it."

QUICK PRESCRIPTION 32

Drive Back Fear

1) Establish physiological control. This means you will influence how your body is functioning. Tense and relax, then let your arms and legs get heavy and warm, then breathe deeply and smile with your whole body. Keep breathing deeply and evenly as you let your muscles relax. Repeat this exercise over and over again until it becomes automatic.
2) Dig to the root of your fear. Identify the one or two factors that represent the real cause of your fearfulness.
3) Imagine for a moment how you would act if you were full of courage. Begin to act that way.
4) Look for ways to eliminate the circumstances that are triggering your fear and go to work on them.

WHEN YOU'RE IN A LOUSY MOOD

You will have days when nothing is amusing and everything is annoying. Ordinary events like waiting for an elevator, motorists taking too long to turn left, or customers in the line who can't decide if they want the decaf or the latte will have you seething. Someone will say, "Good morning!" and you will want to scowl and point out that there's nothing good about it. You are in the grip of a bad mood and it is affecting your response to everything around you.

Try to uncover the reason why you are feeling so miserable. Is it something you ate, a pill you had to take, lack of exercise, or insufficient sleep? Could it be that you are getting the flu, or is it a hormonal imbalance? In other words, is there a physiological reason? Or have you just been through a bad experience? Try to ferret out any physical or otherwise tangible reason for your lousy mood.

If you decide that you're entitled to your lousy mood, you've earned it, and you want to stay in it for a while, that's OK as long as you consciously decide to wallow in it and you make sure that you don't pass it on. Just because you've decided it's a bad day for you is no reason for everyone else to suffer. Take a few minutes to mope or have a little rant or experience the futility of self-pity if you want to. Give yourself a limited (short) time to revel in how black, awful, and stupid everything is, and then regain control of your thoughts and attitudes and move on.

Remember that you have a choice. You can decide to change your feelings. You do this by changing your thoughts. Put your practice of emotional redirection to work for you. Look back for a moment, just long enough to recognize some of the blessings in your life and become enthusiastically thankful for them. Be grateful for everything good in your life. Take nothing for granted. This gratitude is the first step in disrupting your lousy mood.

Think about a time when your head was clear, your mind was brilliant, and great energy was surging through your body. Recall how happy you were. Assume an attitude that corresponds to the way you felt when you were happy. Smile, hold your shoulders back and let them go loose, level, and relaxed. Feel confidence flowing through you. Confidence comes from thinking and acting as a confident person in a particular circumstance. Become an actor and act the part. Let everything that is in your control represent a wonderful mood: the way you answer the phone, the way you deal with people—let it all reflect a wonderful mood and this will send the lousy feeling packing.

If the lousy mood remains, enlist outside resources to help you change your mood. A short, leisurely walk or a good stretch, a look at the wonders of nature, a time-out in your favorite coffee shop, a bouquet of flowers on a gloomy day, or a conversation with someone you love can also help to dispel the clouds that hover around you. Whistle a happy tune. Sing a happy song (if only in your head). Or play your favorite music to put yourself in a better mood. If you don't have any happy mood music, take time to get some or make a recording for the next time a black mood comes your way: choose ten minutes of music that makes you feel energized and happy, and play it when you are down.

Rita arrived late at her office, and her assistant, Maxine, greeted her with a cheery "Good morning!"

"The jury's still out on that one, Max. The six-year-old refused to eat this morning, the eleven-year-old wouldn't get dressed, and the thirty-seven-year-old dashed out the door saying he had an early meeting and couldn't help deliver anyone anywhere. I stepped in a puddle getting back into the car, and then I remembered that my lunch was still in the fridge at home. Oh, and a bird pooped on my new coat on the way in from the parking lot."

"Ahh," said Max, "now there's a five-star morning start. What now? Slam the door and go home?"

"It's a thought. However, the cleaners next door have my coat so I'm here for the day."

Inside her office, Rita eyed a photo of her family in more cooperative times. And another of her son doing his best bug-eyed, tongue-sticking-out face. She stuck out her tongue back at him. "Oh, yeah?" she said. "This is your mother speaking: 'There will be no pop and potato chips on my breakfast menus. Ever!'" She turned to the other photo, "And you, missy, will make up your mind what to wear the night before, and wear it." Eyeing her husband's smiling face, she said darkly, "You owe me. I charge you with desertion on the field of battle.

"Right. Now that I've told everyone what I think, enough already. The former Miss Congeniality is movin' on. 'Heads up, look the world in the eye, and smile, Girls,' as my old cheerleading coach would say."

QUICK PRESCRIPTION 33

Transform Your Mood

1) Acknowledge your bad mood; resolve not to spread it.

2) Establish control of your body—shake any tension out of your arms and legs. Practice **T.A.B.S.**

3) Give yourself a fixed amount of time to be miserable, say, 15 minutes. When moping time is over, tell yourself to "Stop" and visualize the red light going on.

4) Fill your brain with positive thoughts and images of yourself as you want to be.

5) Name three things you can be happily grateful for as you begin to change your feelings.

6) If you have time, stretch or go for a walk, a run, or a workout. Get yourself moving to generate some of those "feel good" hormones.

DEALING WITH DEPRESSION

When you are living in a stressful time—the collapse of a relationship, the long-term illness or death of a loved one, a job loss, a break-in, tough economic times, or some other prolonged difficulty—it is common to feel depressed as well as anxious. Sometimes sadness and depression are understandable responses in distressing times, although there are always things you can do to moderate their effects on your health. If a situation is making you depressed, first deal with yourself—your perception and your responses to what is going on—and then deal with the situation. Remember the power that lies within you.

Stress, anxiety, and depression often coexist and the symptoms overlap. Some of the major symptoms of depression and anxiety are: irritability; uncontrollable worrying; feelings of guilt, restlessness, or fatigue; nervousness; muscle tension; impaired concentration; an inability to enjoy things; and insomnia. If you've been through a major trauma, I am sure that you recognize many of these symptoms. Most of them are familiar to many of us, but only last a short time.

These symptoms, however, can persist and disrupt your life as you struggle with major difficulties, and they will wear you out. The difference between those who suffer from clinical depression and those who do not is often the frequency, severity, and length of time the symptoms are with you and how they alter the underlying chemistry of your body.

Just remember that if you are suffering from severe anxiety or depression, you must seek professional help to get properly assessed and treated. This is particularly true if you are troubled by thoughts of harming yourself or those around you. Clinical depression is not a sign of weakness or an inability to "snap out of it." It has detectable causes and should be treated. There are many drugs that can help lift your depression and improve the quality of your life if they're used under a qualified doctor's care. So, if you are reacting to the stressors of your life with feelings of depression and anxiety, don't feel as if you are alone. There is help available on many fronts. Drug treatment, as well as psychological maneuvers, has changed the lives of many patients. While the quick prescription that follows can help many people, if you try it and it does nothing to help you deal with feelings that are overwhelming you, seek professional help immediately.

Even if you are prescribed drug therapy, be aware that physicians often make the mistake of treating the disease and leaving the patient alone. Once the drug takes effect, doctors tend to become preoccupied with the progress of the treatment. We often ignore the simple psycho-physiological tricks that our patients can practise to feel happier, more energetic, and more in touch with their own inner power. We are so impressed with the positive effects of antidepressants that we fail to give those patients taking medication ways to use their inner power to help them fight depression as an adjunct to drug therapy. Thus, my prescription for depression is applicable even if you are on medication for depression and anxiety. I use antidepressant medication in my practice, but I am always surprised at how much better patients get when they use self-help techniques to bring their own internal power to bear upon the disease as well.

As mentioned again and again in this book, a high level of awareness is a prelude to control over any situation. Therefore, notice your feelings. Actually study them with a view to being able to master them. Know what depression feels like for you. Is it like a knife stabbing you in the chest, a heaviness in your abdomen, or a foggy feeling in your head? Be as specific as possible about the location and the quality of the feeling. What scenarios are playing over and over in your mind?

As before, start to take physical control by practising **T.A.B.S.** (see page 177). In addition to its inherent value, this exercise will keep you in touch with your body and mind, and when the mind and body become as one, you tend to gain control of those distressing, intrusive thoughts that make you feel like a loser.

Next, attend to the reason for your depression. Look at the stressors in your life and try to see what is really causing you grief. What is the heart of the issue? Do a reality check by getting down to the facts and suspending your reaction.

As always, take stock of your blessings. Tell yourself what is good about your life and keep that in mind. Express gratitude in your words, attitude, and actions for all the good things in your life. Some people create a victory list with all the achievements they are proud of. If this appeals to you, take a few minutes and make a list of your achievements and the things in your life that are going well.

Use your resources—anything you have at your disposal that can help you to feel better. Dig deep. Depressing times require serious attention and the deployment of your resources, whether they are personal, professional, or financial. Consider all possibilities—big or small—from finding a new coffee shop to relax in, to giving yourself a break with people you enjoy, or buying some new clothes. When you are depressed, make a deliberate effort to dress better than you normally do. If you have a "rainy day" fund, this is the time to tap into it. This may be the time to go away for the weekend. It may trigger the right attitudinal change in you.

Regardless of your ability to affect the actual situation, take advantage of the fact that you can always change the way you feel. If you are feeling depressed, no doubt you want to feel calmer or happier and more in control. Do this by living consciously in the present. Open your eyes and see what's in front of you. Hear what's around you, and relate your experience to what you want to do with your life. Expand your awareness to help put the current situation into perspective.

Don't accept that you have to feel more and more depressed. While it is hard to take your feelings, thoughts, and attitudes in hand and create the kind of feelings you want, taking action will begin to lead you out of your depression. After taking the first few positive steps, the rest will seem easier. Start now, even if you are down, to work on yourself, because the solution lies within you.

One effective treatment to banish depression is vigorous exercise. Psychiatrists, psychologists, and family doctors in many medical centers use exercise as a major form of treatment for depression. This doesn't have to be a formal workout at a gym. Just remember that movement affects mood. I know a prominent psychiatrist who uses aerobic dance as part of his treatment for depression. I also have adopted exercise in my practice, including fast dancing, as an additional way to fight stress and depression.

News of Ryan and Cheryl's breakup circulated for days before any of Ryan's buddies caught up with him. Keith, the group's breakup specialist, finally got him on the phone.

"How's it going, big guy?"

"Not good. I'm having real trouble this time. I'm ready to settle down and I thought she was 'the one.' I'm not sleeping much, I feel sick half the time, and even though I decided to bury myself in work, I'm starting to have problems keeping up. Any advice?"

"I can tell you what not to do," Keith replied. "Over the years, I've done the party-'til-you-drop 'therapy' and nearly developed a drinking problem. I've treated myself to expensive toys for distraction, and I've done the escape-to-Paradise with hot- and cold-running women. I've had to quit drinking, and the infection is cleared up, thanks to the miracle of antibiotics, but I'm still in debt and will be for a while."

"Great. I was thinking of tapping into my rainy day fund for a wild escape."

"At least you have one of those funds. Maybe that's where I went wrong," Keith said. "Have you considered talking to your doctor or asking for a referral to a counsellor? I'll tell you this: You can run, but you can't hide. Unless you change your head, that black cloud'll be waiting for you when you get back. My experience says you'll end up at your doctor's eventually when this kind of stuff goes down. You might as well start there and save yourself some damage. In the meantime, the guys are going up north to cut some trail and get scratched and bitten and filthy and generally exhaust ourselves. Want to come along?"

"Yeah, I do. And thanks. I'm lucky to have you guys around."

QUICK PRESCRIPTION 34

Overcome Depression

1) Get professional help in assessing your depression—start with your physician—and follow the treatment prescribed.

2) Acknowledge your feelings and your situation, but, no matter how terrible things are, make a decision to feel better. Resolve to work at making yourself feel better.

3) Practice instant relaxation constantly. Use any sad thoughts as a cue to practice **T.A.B.S.** to keep your body relaxed and your mind clear.

   - **T**ense and relax your muscles for a few seconds
   - **A**rms and legs become heavy and warm
   - **B**reathe deeply and evenly
   - **S**mile and relax your body

4) Look after your body by eating a balanced diet—use food as part of your medicine. Avoid fat and refined carbohydrates; pile on the fruits and vegetables. Be physically active every day with exercise that benefits your heart. Go to bed at a regular time and get at least 7 hours of sleep every night.

5) Be aware of and fight any negative emotions that you are experiencing—you can't let them burden you. Replace them with hope for the future, inner peace, confidence, joy, and love. Begin by acting as if you feel these emotions. Act to convince yourself as well as others.

6) Say thanks more often and more enthusiastically. Start noticing every little benefit in your life. Think and act as if you are the most grateful person in the world.

THE PURSUIT OF HAPPINESS

WE USUALLY THINK of happiness as an emotional state that results from something that has happened to us, like winning some money, buying something we really want, getting a significant promotion, or falling in love. The fact is that *Happiness Is an Inside Job*, as John Powell says in his book of the same title. You have to take responsibility to make yourself happy. No one can do that for you. You carry your own happiness with you whether you are up on a mountain or down in a valley. The French philosopher, Voltaire, said, "Paradise is where I am." Smile when things are bad, act as if you are happy, treat people as though they are special, and you too can say, "Paradise is where I am."

We often overlook the relevance of happiness in the workplace. It is as if we think that happiness is out of place in the hard world of business. At best, we regard it as a little bonus that sometimes comes our way. The fact is that happy employees perform better, happy athletes do better on the field, and happy patients recover faster from surgery or disease.

According to Nathaniel Brandon in his work on *Inner Strength*, happiness is the natural order of things. It is relevant and important at all times, and it is very fortunate that you have the power to generate happiness whenever you like. The purpose of your life is to enjoy it, and you must not allow circumstances to block your enjoyment of life. You can learn to summon happiness and enjoy the moments of your life, and you can do this despite any difficulties that surround you.

When you are in the throes of a predicament, the last emotion that comes to mind is happiness. Yet happiness is an effective antidote to stress, but how happy you are depends on you. Father, mother, sister, brother, and lover may try to make you happy, but unless you choose happiness, all other efforts are in vain.

When you miss the flight that was taking you to your long-awaited Caribbean vacation, when you discover that you have been the target of the malicious company gossip, or when your car runs out of gas on your way to an important appointment, remember that happiness is a choice. You can choose to embrace the emotion of happiness right there despite what is going on.

Whenever a stressor raises its head, unhappiness is never far behind and you should get into the habit of inducing feelings of happiness to combat any stress reaction.

Assume the role of a happy person. Even if you are unhappy, act as if you are happy. The attitude will produce the feelings. Emotions have a corresponding chemistry. They put their stamp on your physiology and by now, you know that you can change the emotion by changing the stamp—by acting out the opposite emotion. When you laugh, you not only move your facial and belly muscles, you change your chemistry as well. You can always induce the feelings of happiness by doing things or thinking as you would if you were happy.

Ask yourself the questions, "If I were happy right now, how would I feel? What would I be thinking? What would my posture be like? How would I be breathing? Would I be smiling? How would I respond to the people around me?"

Behave as if you were truly happy and you will trigger feelings of happiness. If your life is stressful and a lot of negativity is in the air, hum a happy song or whistle a happy tune in the face of the unhappiness. Laugh and smile more than you ever did, and concentrate on what is good about your life. Share a good joke when you hear one. Shower someone with compliments and share in their good feelings. The real message is that you can make yourself happy and happiness is a powerful antidote to stress.

Lisa and the kids were watching a TV special about the developing world when one of the kids asked the big question: "Mom, they don't have movies or cellphones or cars even. How come they're laughing so much of the time?"

"I guess they're happy," she said.

The kids weren't buying it. "How can they be? They don't have anything!"

"Maybe you don't need things to be happy. Maybe being happy is about something else entirely, guys. They have enough to eat; they're playing with their friends; they're with their families. Maybe even though it's really nice to have lots of things, you don't need them to be happy. Think about that one, and then we'll talk about it some more later, OK?"

QUICK PRESCRIPTION 35

Rx

Get a Merry Heart

1) Decide that happiness is your birthright.

2) Assume the role of a happy person. Sing, hum a happy tune, or make a tape of music that triggers happy emotions and play it. Remember, according to Dr. James Loehr of the Institute of Health and Human Performance in Orlando, Florida, "Music moves physiology."

3) Put yourself in an environment that will trigger pleasant feelings: pleasant people, nice surroundings.

4) Breathe deep, relaxing breaths, and exercise—movement will change your emotions.

5) Get involved in helping other people with their problems. That alone can break your unhappy mood.

6) Don't forget to smile.

SUMMING UP

YOU NOW KNOW what you can do to master the stress in your life. Not the stressors, but the stress. You will still encounter bad days, frustrating clients, occasionally obstinate or defiant children, traffic jams, computers that crash—you know what your stressors are. The good news is that these things no longer have the power to make you sick, if you choose to exercise your power to master your response to them. This is the exciting news I have been sharing with you—stress is the response and you can choose your response. Wow!

The 35 Quick Prescriptions have shown you how to:

- Live with awareness by bringing a higher level of consciousness to your life and work.
- Perceive yourself as a winner no matter what the situation.
- Take charge of your response.
- Take control of your physiology.
- Use your choice of several techniques we've covered to build mental toughness and make yourself hardy against stress.
- Stress-proof yourself for life.

These skills will require regular practice before they become new habits. You have no doubt lived with some aspects of the stress reaction for most of your life and it will take time to change the way you are programmed. You are currently programmed for muscle tension, hormone rushes, negative emotions, and a mind that just won't stop chattering. I am asking you to work hard on a continuing basis to change your responses to the stressors in your life.

The checkups and prescriptions in this book are designed to help you build awareness and give you the skills to master your response to stressors. Once you've reviewed them and practised them, your skills will be honed in the following key stress response areas:

- Your breathing
- Your muscles
- Your emotions

You will be able to program your breathing to keep it slow, relax your muscles and make them heavy and warm, and generate positive emotions so you can remain calm, peaceful, optimistic, and happy in stressful situations. Use the reminder summaries on the pages that follow to help you in your daily practice. Photocopy them and keep them wherever you're most likely to practise them.

Once you've mastered the instant relaxation techniques, buy some stickers—stars or rainbows or whatever appeals to you—and put them around you to remind you to do the exercises regularly during the day. Put one on the clock on your desk or in the kitchen, and, when you are in a hurry, it will remind you to slow down, take a deep breath, and go for effectiveness instead of speed. Put one on the phone (and on your cellphone), one on your computer or your fridge, all to remind you to make the process of instant relaxation a regular part of every day. Or write the acronym **T.A.B.S.** on pieces of paper and put one in your purse or pocket, one on your desk, and one on the dashboard of your car. Put them around any place that you frequent to remind yourself to take time for harmony, health, and relaxation in your body and mind.

If you practise these techniques and make them your own, you will never, ever be stressed out again.

TAKE A "BREATH BREAK"

Once you've mastered abdominal breathing, take regular "breath breaks" for a few minutes.

1) Sit in a comfortable, upright position.

2) Put one hand, palm down, on your abdomen, two inches below your navel.

3) Breathe in slowly, pushing your hand out; and breathe out slowly, letting your abdomen (and your hand) sink for a few minutes.

4) Say to yourself, "Breathing in, I observe my body and mind," and, "Breathing out, I smile and relax."

RELAXATION REMINDER— THE INSTANT EXERCISE

Do regular muscle-tension detection sweeps, and take 20-second breaks several times during the day to:

1) Take a deep, slow breath and tense your muscles for a few seconds.

2) Relax and smile as you breathe out and feel your arms and legs becoming heavy and warm.

3) Repeat the tense/relax three times.

4) Focus on breathing in and out, feeling a wave of relaxation coming over you every time you exhale.

INSTANT EMOTIONAL TRANSFORMATION

1) If you have been hit by a stressful situation, notice and name the main negative emotion that you are feeling right now (fear, worry, anger, etc.). Know that it is eroding your health, so take control quickly.

2) Say to yourself, "This too will pass and until it does, I refuse to let it compromise my health."

3) Replace the negative emotion first with gratitude: name one or more things that you are grateful for.

4) Use your preferred techniques to move your emotional state to a better place. Choose from hope, enthusiasm, confidence, compassion, love, joy, and inner peace and harmony by revisiting great memories, gazing at your visual aids, playing your music, or adopting the actions of someone who feels the way you want to feel.

MORNING AND EVENING STRESS-PROOFING

Take a few minutes to give yourself the gift of relaxation in the morning and again in the evening.

In the morning use the **General Relaxation Exercise:**

1) Take ten minutes to reflect on who you are and why you are here. Use some of that early morning time to appreciate what you have and set your "gratitude attitude" for the day.

2) Do a minute of abdominal breathing. As you breathe in, say to yourself, "Breathing in, I observe my body and my mind," and as you breathe out, say, "Breathing out, I smile and let all my muscles relax."

3) Focus your attention on your toes, and say to yourself, "Toes relax"; then take another slow, deep breath and say, "Feet relax." Move systematically up your legs with every breath, relaxing your calves, knees, thighs, and moving right on up your body to your abdomen, your chest, and your shoulders, through your hands, arms, neck, and head. Concentrate on each area as you go and feel the relaxation rise in your system.

At the end of the day, you may need to practise **Draining Tension Away:**

1) Imagine that your toes are removable stoppers screwed on to the end of your feet. Imagine your body as a container filled with liquid representing fatigue and tension.

2) Unscrew your toes and visualize all the tension in your body flowing out through the openings in your feet. Let every drop of tension go. Feel it happening and visualize it in your mind.

3) Screw your toes back on again. Imagine pouring golden, liquid relaxation into your body through an opening at the top of your head. Feel the relaxation rise from your feet, filling up your legs and rising steadily up your body to completely saturate your body and mind with feelings of relaxation and happiness.